Applied ergonomics han

C000274299

Edited by
I. A. R. Galer
Scientific Director, Institute for Consumer Ergonomics,
Loughborough University of Technology

BUTTERWORTHS
London Boston Singapore Sydney Toronto Wellington

PART OF REED INTERNATIONAL P.L.C.

First published 1987
  Reprinted 1989

© **Butterworth & Co. Publishers Ltd 1987**

British Library Cataloguing in Publication Data

Galer, I.A.R.
Applied ergonomics handbook.—2nd ed.
1. Human engineering
I. Title
620.8′2   TA166
ISBN 0–408–00880–6

Library of Congress Cataloging in Publication Data

Galer, I.A.R.
  Applied ergonomics handbook.

  Bibliography:p.
  Includes index.
  1. Human engineering—Handbooks, manuals, etc.
  I. Title
  T59.7.G354 1987   620.8′2   86–28335
  ISBN 0–408–00880–6

Photoset by Katerprint Typesetting Services, Oxford
Printed and bound in Great Britain by Butler & Tanner, Frome, Somerset

Introduction and acknowledgements

This book was first published in 1974 under the title *Applied Ergonomics Handbook* as a compilation of a series of booklets on Ergonomics for Industry, edited and revised by B. Shackel and printed in the journal *Applied Ergonomics*.

The original booklets were produced by the Department of Scientific and Industrial Research and, later, by the Ministry of Technology, and were: *The Industrial use of ergonomics* by W. T. Singleton; *Instruments and people* by B. Shackel and D. Whitfield; *Design of work for the disabled* by S. Griew; *Inspection and human efficiency* by R. M. Belbin; *Ergonomics versus accidents* by R. G. Sell; *Noise in industry* by D. E. Broadbent; *Men, machines and controls* by K. A. Provins; *Thermal comfort in industry* by R. H. Fox; *Lighting of work places* by J. Longmore; *Seating in industry* by P. Branton; *Layout of workspaces* by J. C. Jones; and *Current trends towards systems design* by W. T. Singleton. Chapter 14 of the original book was written by K. F. H. Murrell.

This book is a much revised version of the 1974 edition. The revisions have been made to update details of the text, to change the order of some chapters and to merge others, and to add new material. The book is intended to appeal to a wide range of readers, in industry, commerce, education, and other areas. It is introductory in nature, though references are made to other, more detailed, sources covering particular areas of ergonomics.

I should like to offer my thanks in particular to a number of colleagues who have devoted their time and expertise in revising some of the chapters: M. D. Galer (The design of displays); K. C. Parsons (The environment—climatic factors); J. Sandover (The environment—noise and vibration); P. T. Stone (The environment—vision and lighting); and K. D. Eason (Work organisation and job design). I would also like to thank Prof. N. S. Kirk, Joint Scientific Editor of the journal *Applied Ergonomics*, for his valuable assistance in selecting the case studies which are reprinted in Chapter 11. However, the responsibility for any errors in the text is mine.

I. A. R. Galer
Loughborough, 1986

Notes on the contributors

Ian A. R. Galer, BSc, MSc, FErgS, is the Scientific Director of the Institute for Consumer Ergonomics at Loughborough University. Previously he was a Lecturer in Ergonomics and Psychology in the Department of Human Sciences at the University. His interests lie in the areas of transport ergonomics, product design, ergonomics and industrial design, and psychological measurement.

Kenneth D. Eason, BTech, PhD, ABPS, is the Reader in Cognitive Ergonomics in the Department of Human Sciences at Loughborough University, where he was previously a Senior Lecturer. He is also a Director of the HUSAT Research Centre in the Department. His interests lie in the areas of work organisation and job design, software systems design, and the implementation of information technology.

Margaret D. Galer, BSc, MSc, PhD, ABPS, FErgS, is the ESPRIT Project Manager at the HUSAT Research Centre, Department of Human Sciences at Loughborough University. She was previously a Principal Research Officer in the Institute for Consumer Ergonomics at the University. Her interests lie in the areas of transport ergonomics, and the Human Factors aspects of information technology applications.

N. Stuart Kirk, BA, PhD, is Professor and Head of the Department of Human Sciences at Loughborough University. He is also the Director of the Institute for Consumer Ergonomics at the University and is the Joint Scientific Editor of the journal *Applied Ergonomics*. His interests are in consumer ergonomics, product design, information display, and the ergonomics aspects of computer systems.

Kenneth C. Parsons, BSc, PGCE, PhD, is a Lecturer in Ergonomics in the Department of Human Sciences at Loughborough University. He was previously at the Institute of Sound and Vibration Research at Southampton University. He is an Assistant Scientific Editor of the journal *Applied Ergonomics*. His interests are in the effects of the thermal environment on Man, and in the design of expert systems to model these effects.

Jack Sandover, BSc, PhD, CEng, MIMechE, FErgS, is a Lecturer in the Department of Human Sciences at Loughborough University. His interests are in the effects of noise and vibration on Man, transport ergonomics, biomechanics, and the study of back pain.

Peter T. Stone, BSc, FCIBSE, FErgS, ABPS, is the Reader in Vision and Lighting in the Department of Human Sciences at Loughborough University. He is also Chairman of the Lighting Division of CIBSE. His interests are in the relationship between light and its effects on people, the design of the lit environment, and the lighting requirements of partially sighted people.

Contents

Chapter 1

Ergonomics— Introduction and applications

In this chapter the subject of ergonomics is introduced, and its main areas of application, the human characteristics studied, and the role of the ergonomist in industry and commerce are discussed.

Ergonomics

People spend most of their time engaged in the performance of tasks. Tasks are activities with specified goals, and may be paid or unpaid. Tasks are carried out in the home, at work, on the road, in leisure and sport, and on the battlefield. Thus a task may involve setting up and operating an industrial lathe, using a computer, digging a hole with a garden spade, or driving a motor car. Very many tasks are carried out by a person using some tool or machine; the machine is employed in order to extend human ability, to enable people to do things they cannot do unaided, or to make the task easier to perform.

The tools and machines used in the performance of tasks must be suited to their users. A chair must be the correct height for the occupant, a computer language must be understandable, and the displays on a car dashboard must be readable by the driver. Even the size of a garden spade must fit the size of the gardener. If this fit is achieved, we may expect the performance of the user to be better than would be the case if it were not.

Traditionally, tools and machines were made by their eventual users: the craftsman would design and make tools that suited his exact purposes, rather than acquiring tools from a specialist maker. This bespoke manufacture of relatively simple devices allowed the tool to fit its user exactly—it would be fitted as the design progressed, and modifications to its shape and size could be made as the craftsman gradually evolved the tool. More recently, the design and manufacture of tools and machines has devolved to specialists, and we have seen a rapid development in the engineering sciences and technologies as a reflection of this. One consequence of this development, however, is that the maker and the user of a tool are no longer the same person, and the maker must make assumptions about the user's characteristics in an attempt to achieve a satisfactory fit between user and product.

1

For many years a measure of common sense on the part of the engineer and designer was sufficient to fit user and tool in an acceptable manner: as long as the tool was relatively simple, and as long as the consequences of poor fit were not severe, the problem was not a difficult one to solve. In recent years, however, Man has used tools and machines of increasing complexity, and users may be placed in increasingly hazardous environments as a result; aircraft provide rich examples of this, where a complex machine (the aircraft itself) is used to transport the user through a very dangerous environment where the consequences of a failure or inadequacy of the machine are life threatening. Additionally, as more and more products compete in a fiercely competitive market, it is becoming essential that a given product surpass its rivals in every respect. One such respect is its usability, complementing others such as engineering excellence, cost, and aesthetics. Related to this is the need for mass-produced articles to be correctly designed at the outset, rather than passing through a long and expensive series of modifications. Finally, because of better health care and improved living conditions, people may now expect to live longer than previously, and the population contains many people with various degrees of physical and mental impairment who may not have survived in past times. As a result, the designer of tools and machines must now cater for a market containing extremes of age, health, and physical and mental ability; that is, one whose members are much more variable than they used to be.

Table 1.1 Contrasts between the design and use of 'traditional' and present-day tools and machines

'Traditional' tools and machines	*Present-day tools and machines*
Relatively simple	Increasingly complex
Made by the user	Made by a manufacturer
Small number made	Large number made
Trivial consequences of design error	Profound consequences of design error
Product competitiveness unimportant	Marketing competitiveness vital
Characteristics of the user population fairly restricted	Wide variation in user population

All these factors (summarised in Table 1.1) have led to a recognition that the fit between user and machine or tool is important and cannot reliably be solved by recourse to common sense. An area of study and application has developed which is devoted to the problem of fit, and has the name 'ergonomics'. (In some countries, notably the USA, the term 'human factors' is used instead of 'ergonomics'. The two have the same meaning.) It is scientific, in that ergonomists measure human characteristics and human function, and establish the way that the human body and the human mind work. It is also technological, in that the results of scientific work in the human sciences are applied by ergonomists in the solution of practical problems in the design and manufacture of products and systems. The word 'ergonomics' was derived from two Greek words, 'ergon' and 'nomos', which together mean 'the laws of work'. Work, however, should be taken in a broad context, in the same way as products and systems may include kitchen sinks, computers, and public buses as well as lathes and screwdrivers.

Ergonomics is not a brand new science. As we have noted, the use of common sense, systematically applied, can result in good ergonomics solutions. Similarly, many improvements in working conditions, and in the selection and training of workers, have resulted from studies by industrial psychologists and physiologists during the early part of this century. There is even a claim that the term 'ergonomics' was first used in Eastern Europe in the nineteenth century. However, it was not until the early 1940s, and wartime, that the practical engineering approach came together with the academic, human scientific approach on a reasonably large scale. The impetus behind this development was the change in design of aircraft and weapons which were capable of operation at greater speeds and at greater accuracies than hitherto; this placed a greater load on the operator in an environment where errors had to be avoided at all costs and where a minimum of training was desirable. Thus it proved necessary to bring together two groups of specialists: those who knew about human capacities and those who knew about machines. Anatomists, physiologists, and experimental psychologists worked together with engineers to make user-plus-machine an effective fighting weapon. The success of this teamwork resulted in the continued support for, and an extension of, ergonomics research and application in the armed services.

Since the early development of the subject, its application has widened to include many areas other than military endeavour. Currently, ergonomists advise on both the products of industry and on the processes that generate these products; on the design of working environments in industrial and commercial applications; on the structure of dialogues between computers and their users as well as on the design of the hardware itself; in the production of domestic equipment and consumer products; in the design and development of cars, aircraft, trains, and ships; and in the design, not only of tools and machines, but also of people's jobs. In each of these areas, however, the approach is the same: to achieve a good fit between people and the hardware and facilities they use.

Consequences of not using ergonomics

The fact that people are able to use poorly designed equipment, often under difficult working conditions, does not mean that the most efficient use is being made of the production unit, in terms of either human effort or the quality of the product of this effort. At the same time, however, everyday experience will tell us that a product need not be specifically designed for an individual user for its operation to be acceptable: small departures from the 'optimal' solution can easily be tolerated. For example, clothing need not fit exactly for it to be comfortable and functional; the chairs we sit on may be a little too low or a little too high and still be acceptably comfortable; the lighting levels in a room may be slightly lower than we would like but this does not stop us from reading a book. The important point here is that people are adaptable: they can tolerate small departures from optimal designs of the equipment they use and the environments they live and work in. This adaptation may take a little time in some cases, but the total change is small and may not even be noticed by the individual. Were people not adaptable, every product or facility that a person uses would have to be built specifically for that person.

There is, however, a limit to the amount of adaptation a person may reasonably be asked to make. Some products and facilities may be so unsuited to the user that the task is impossible to perform. In this case, no amount of adaptation will enable it to be done, and the user might suffer physical harm or extreme frustration in an effort to compensate for the poor design. In less extreme cases, adaptation may result in the task being achieved, but at the expense of stress and strain on the user. This may be manifested in an increase in the time taken and in the number of errors made, as well as a feeling of dissatisfaction or discomfort on the part of the user (Figs 1.1 and 1.2). If the user is attempting to use a marketed product such as a food mixer, the difficulty of use experienced is likely to affect the market success of the product. In addition, errors, even if they are rare, can have serious consequences leading to personal injury and sometimes death. There is some evidence that even modest adaptation over long periods of time, such as working in an environment that vibrates continually at a low level, may have long-term effects on the health of the

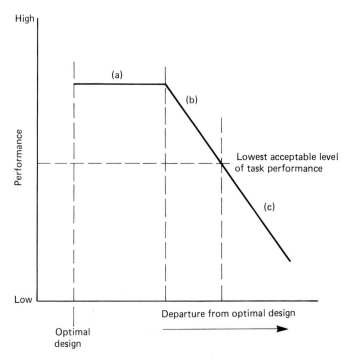

Figure 1.1 Design, adaptation, and task performance: in area (a) maximum performance is maintained by means of successful adaptation; in area (b) adaptation cannot compensate for design deficiencies, and, although performance is acceptable, the task involves a degree of strain or discomfort; in area (c) the design is so unsuitable that the task is dangerous or impossible to perform to an acceptable level.

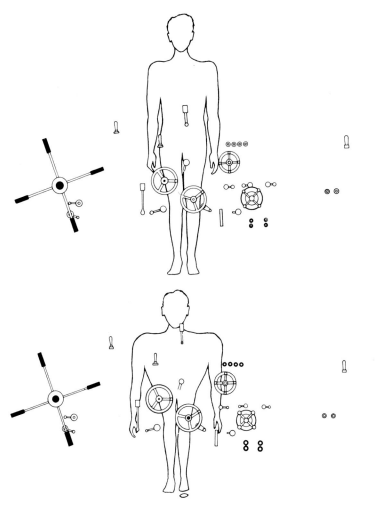

Figure 1.2 The controls of a lathe in current use are not within easy reach of the average man, but are so placed that the ideal operator should be 1372 mm ($4\frac{1}{2}$ ft) tall, 610 mm (2 ft) across the shoulders, and have a 2348 mm (8 ft) arm span.

individual. The problem here is that the person may not experience discomfort or inconvenience, because the adaptation has occurred smoothly and gradually; thus, adaptation is not always desirable.

In summary, therefore, ignorance of ergonomics by designers, planners, and other decision makers can result in a poor fit between user, equipment, and environment. This is manifested in the time taken to carry out tasks with the equipment, in mistakes being made, and in feelings of discomfort and dissatisfaction in the user. The user may suffer temporary or permanent physical damage. On a wider scale, marketed products are uncompetitive, national resources may be squandered, and absenteeism and labour turnover rates increase as a workforce becomes dissatisfied with its working conditions and practices.

Areas of study in ergonomics

For descriptive purposes, ergonomics can be seen as applying to a number of aspects of the interaction between people and the world about them. These aspects will be described briefly here, and are covered in more detail in later chapters. They are summarised in Table 1.2.

Table 1.2 Main areas of study in ergonomics

Area of study	Examples
Physical aspects of the user–machine interface	Size, shape, colour, texture and method of operation of displays and controls for cars, domestic appliances, industrial and commercial equipment, etc.
Cognitive aspects of the user–machine interface	Understanding of instructions and other information; style of dialogue between computer and user
Workplace design and workspace layout	Layout of offices, factories, domestic kitchens, public spaces, etc; detailed relationships between furniture and equipment, and between different equipment components
Physical environment	Effects of climate, noise and vibration, illumination, and chemical/biological contaminants on human performance and health
Psychological environment	Organisational structure within a group and its effects on satisfaction with the task, productivity and group membership
Job design, selection and training	Effects of shiftwork on performance; design of instructions, job aids and training schemes; selection of personnel against criteria of aptitude and personality

Physical aspects of the user–machine interface. The user of a machine must be able to control the machine. In order to do this, the user must know the state the machine is in, and must be able to change that state. These two tasks are carried out by means of displays and controls, respectively. For example, a driver will look at the instruments in the car to find out the speed of the vehicle, the amount of fuel in the tank, the temperature of the engine coolant, and a variety of other information. In addition, the car is controlled by means of the steering wheel, the foot pedals, and the minor controls for lights, direction indicators, windscreen wipers, and the like. Displays and controls, of varying degrees of sophistication, are found in all products and equipment. If their size, shape, colour, texture, method of operation, and other physical characteristics prevent or hinder their easy operation by the user, then they are deficient in ergonomics terms, and amenable to ergonomics analysis and improvement.

Cognitive aspects of the user–machine interface. A visual display, such as a direction sign, may be visible—that is, its physical characteristics may be satisfactory from an ergonomics viewpoint—but it may not be understandable. Since information is transferred from user to machine and vice versa at the interface, it is essential that this information can be comprehended by the user. This is an ergonomics problem in the same way as the physical characteristics of controls and displays are ergonomics problems. The general problem may be described as a 'cognitive' one, because the word refers to knowledge and understanding. It is as important to achieve a cognitive fit between user and machine as it is to achieve a physical fit. Much of the current interest in the interaction between people and computers is based on cognitive questions rather than physical ones.

Workspace design and workplace layout. The idea of physical fit between user and equipment can be extended from the design of displays and controls, to include the chairs we sit on, the space inside the cars we drive, the layout of factory floors and control rooms, and so forth. A number of factors are involved here, mainly concerned with the physical relationships between people and equipment, but on a larger scale than the design of individual displays and controls. For example, if a person needs to consult more than one display, or use more than one control in the operation of a machine, then those controls and displays need to be of compatible design, and must be located in such a way as to allow easy transition from one to the other. Even single displays must be visible or audible, and controls must be reachable. Whether this is so depends, clearly, on where they are located in the work area or workspace. Similarly, different pieces of equipment in a work area, whether it be a domestic kitchen or the bridge of a ship, should be compatible in their design, location, and operation. Allowance must sometimes be made for more than one person to use equipment at the same time, or to work in the same general area. Principles of workplace layout might also be applied to the design of auditoriums, pedestrian precincts, and other large spaces.

The physical environment. All activities take place in some environment, the characteristics of which may be expressed in terms of its climate (hot/cold, draughty/stagnant, dry/humid), the amount of noise and vibration, and the nature and amount of illumination. Research, as well as everyday experience, has shown that these environmental factors are an important determinant of the effectiveness with which equipment and machines are used, and they are thus an important area of study in ergonomics. Furthermore, since, for example, very high noise levels can become a hazard to health rather than merely a nuisance, ergonomists are concerned with the minimisation of other health hazards, such as those due to ionising radiation and chemical and biological pollution.

The psychological environment. The circumstances under which people work—the structure of the organisation and the role of the individual—may be seen as an environment in a similar way to the physical environment. This 'psychological environment' will have profound effects on the attitudes of working people, their satisfaction in work, the quality and quantity of the output, and, eventually, the success of the company or other organisation. As with physical factors, it is necessary to ensure a 'fit' between the expectations and attitudes of workers in factories, banks, offices, and shops, and the organisational characteristics of these places; as such, this is yet another area of ergonomics activity.

Job design, selection and training. Closely related to the design of the psychological environment is the problem of designing jobs that fit people, as well as organisations. Studies of human performance at different tasks, at different times of day, with different periods of work and rest, as well as the way in which physical and cognitive skills are acquired, and the satisfaction with which they are viewed, lead to recommendations about job design, training and instruction procedures, and the provision of aids to the completion of tasks. Whilst the ergonomist will normally prefer to design or modify the characteristics of a machine or procedure to fit its user, it is sometimes necessary to 'alter' the human user by means of selection, training, and the use of job aids.

In summary, ergonomics is the problem of fitting people to the equipment and processes they use. Preferably, this is done by 'fitting the task to the user' rather than 'fitting the user to the task', although both strategies may be employed. The task is described in physical terms (controls, displays, workspaces, and environments) as well as psychological ones (understanding, satisfaction, responsibility). The fundamental assumption is that performance will be better and more satisfying if this fit is good than if it is poor.

Criteria in assessing ergonomics problems and solutions

The idea of 'poor fit' has been mentioned several times above, and it is necessary to state clearly the ways in which poor, or good, fit may be recognised in practice. These are summarised in Table 1.3.

Table 1.3 Indicators of poor fit between task and user

Level 1	Quality and quantity of output
	Quantity of output per unit time
Level 2	Periods of absence because of illness or dissatisfaction
	Underuse of products or equipment
	Accidents or critical incidents
	Complaints and criticism or products and environments

The consequences of good and poor fit may be considered at two main levels. The first and most obvious indication is the output from the user–machine system: if output is lower than might be expected, or if its quality is unacceptable, or if insufficient output per unit time is being made, then this might be due to poor fit, and an ergonomics investigation may be required. This description applies most readily to the production of goods in a factory by a worker or workers in conjunction with machines. In this environment, terms such as 'machines' and 'output' can easily be imagined. However, it can be applied to any user–machine combination, such as someone using a typewriter, domestic food preparation equipment, a motor car, or a set of instructions for a lawn mower. The question in each case is 'Is the task being done as quickly and as accurately as we wish?'.

At the second level, however, deficiencies in the quality and quantity of the output may be complemented and supplemented by information about the human element in the user–machine system. Poor fit may be due to the physical relationship between user and machine. Sometimes this is manifested in periods of absence, when the user is in paid employment (if the task is an unpaid one, mere lack of use of the machine or facility will be equivalent to absence); absence itself may be due to occupational illness, or to low levels of job satisfaction. Job satisfaction, however, may also be due to the organisational aspects of the task, such as the amount of responsibility it carries, the amount of satisfaction in the task, or the amount of personal contact the individual has with his or her colleagues. A further physical indication may be the number of accidents that occur, some of which may result in temporary or permanent disability.

Thus an ergonomics investigation may begin with examination of output or usage records, reports of errors and mistakes, complaints from employees or consumers about the performance of the machine or product, and analyses of accidents. In a situation where a completely new product or facility is being developed, rather than an existing one being studied and modified, these factors will be used as criteria in the evaluation of mockups and prototypes.

When it comes to a closer examination of the reasons for unacceptable levels of output, errors, complaints, and accidents, a further level of analysis is required. This is discussed in the next chapter.

Human characteristics relevant to ergonomics

We have seen that fit between user and machine or facility can be described broadly in physical, psychological, and biological terms. Within these areas it is useful to consider exactly those human characteristics that are measured and used by the ergonomist; they constitute the basic data for ergonomics work and the solutions that flow from this.

Physical characteristics. We are concerned here largely with the size and shape of the human body, and its strength, in both structural and functional terms. Thus we wish to know how tall people are, and how height varies within the population and between different populations, such as peoples of different nationalities. Information on body size is not, of course, confined to height: data might be sought on something as detailed as hand breadth or finger length if the aim is to design gloves, or shoulder width if we are concerned with the design of escape hatches for battle tanks. In addition to data about body dimensions (known as static anthropometry) we also need information on how these dimensions affect human performance: for instance, the distance a person can reach with the arm will be related to arm length but will not equal arm length. So 'dynamic' or functional anthropometry as a related field will provide further useful information (Fig 1.3). Data on body weight and shape accompany anthropometric data, as do those describing human strength, both in terms of the loads that can be applied to the body without damaging it and of the forces that can be generated by the body, in different positions and for different periods of time. The study of human body movement and human strength is known as 'biomechanics'.

Psychological characteristics. The term 'psychological' is open to several interpretations, but for the present it may be regarded as comprising three main areas. The first relates to the human sensory system: how big an

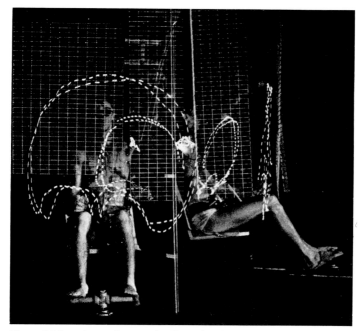

Figure 1.3 In order to discover the dimensional requirements of a man in action, the Engineering Research Institute of the University of Michigan conducted a series of experiments in which flashing lamps were attached to the hand and arm of a seated man. As he moved his body and arms, a photographic record was made. From this, 'contour maps' were compiled, marking the edge of the space reached by hands and feet at various levels. (Source: Anthropology Section, Aerospace Medical Research Laboratories, Wright-Patterson Air Force Base, Ohio, USA)

object must be before it can be seen; what colours can be discriminated easily; how much contrast there must be between a figure and its background for the figure to be seen; how loud a sound must be for it to be heard; how sensitive the hearing system is to different sound frequencies; that is, a whole range of issues all concerned with the senses of touch, taste, smell, vision, and hearing. The second area deals with the cognitive system, and includes knowledge of the nature of human memory, the way that patterns are interpreted, human ability to form conceptual associations, the effect of attention and concentration on the processing of information, the development and power of attitudes and opinions, and the way that people make decisions. The final area deals with the psychological factors in motor performance (rather than biomechanical factors), and is concerned with human reaction times to different stimuli, the way that manual skills are acquired, the levels of skill that can be reached and the amount of practice necessary to maintain that skill, as well as the performance of non-manual tasks, such as speech.

Biological characteristics. Ergonomists are interested in the way that the components of the human body operate, to a great extent because it is possible to use physiological measures to assess the value of ergonomics solutions. For example, intense electrical activity in a muscle can mean that the muscle is stressed, perhaps in maintaining a working posture. Heart rate and blood pressure measurements can also be used to see whether the body as a whole is being stressed in the execution of a task. Galvanic skin response (the basis of the so-called 'lie detector') has been used as a measure of psychological arousal and attention. At another level, knowledge of, for instance, the way that muscles work and the mechanism by which they become fatigued, or the way in which food is digested and absorbed, and even the daily variation in performance due to biological rhythms, are all of use in the specification of tasks and in the determination of work/rest cycles for sequences of tasks.

Where are ergonomists to be found?

An organisation which perceives itself to have an ergonomics problem in the products and services it generates, or in its own working structure, will be faced with a basic decision: to use its own ergonomics expertise, or to bring in expertise from some outside agency.

The organisation will normally need to be relatively large to justify employing an ergonomist full time, even though ergonomics can be applied to a wide variety of problems within the organisation. If this course of action is taken, however, there are still a number of ways in which the ergonomist can work.

It is possible, first, for a special ergonomics department or unit to be established. This is done in a number of organisations, and the unit acts as an 'internal consultant' to the other departments, working with designers, engineers, architects, managers, health and safety experts, and the like. In some cases, the ergonomics unit may also carry out work for other organisations as well as its own.

In other organisations, however, the ergonomist is located within some other department, and will usually be concerned with a smaller range of problems than those encountered by the general ergonomics unit. Established departments, whose interests and activities are allied to ergonomics, are reviewed briefly below.

Design and production engineering. It is through collaboration with the engineer and the designer responsible for the design of production systems, capital equipment or consumer products, that ergonomics finds an important role. The ergonomist provides the engineer with data on human dimensions and human ability, with scientific methods to obtain such exact information as may be required, and with techniques to validate its application to a specific problem. These data enable the engineer to take the user-centred approach to the problem, and to make proper decisions about the tasks to be assigned to the machine and the user. This contrasts with the traditional approach of using cost and practicality as the sole design criteria. It is worth emphasising again that there are many functions, such as versatility, detection and interpretation of information, where human ability at present far exceeds machine ability.

Work study. Where work study is well established, the ergonomist can provide a very useful supplementary aid to production efficiency. Ergonomics can be applied to production problems, modifications to existing machinery and workplaces, and the control of the working environment. With the passage of time, production methods are likely to change, and equipment used for purposes for which it was not originally designed. The ergonomist uses the same task analysis procedures as the work study practitioner, but extends the analysis to cover the cognitive as well as the physical aspects of the job.

Medicine and occupational health. Ergonomics and occupational medicine are both concerned with the health and safety of industrial and commercial workers. It may be argued that their interests are slightly different in that the ergonomist attempts to reduce or eliminate accidents and industrial disease before these occur, by means of proper design of the working environment, the workplace, and working procedures. The specialist in occupational medicine may be more concerned with the consequences of accidents and disease, and with the rehabilitation of individuals who have suffered them. The distinction, however, is not a clear one: occupational health specialists take an increasing interest in the prevention of accidents and disease, using methods and data supplied by the ergonomist. At the same time, ergonomists have been involved in programmes and in equipment design for the rehabilitation of people disabled by industrial or other injury.

Personnel. It has been pointed out that fit between user and machine may be achieved by changing the machine or by changing the user. Whilst the latter strategy is not generally as desirable as the former, it is often necessary to adopt it for practical purposes. It is thus possible to find an ergonomist working in the personnel department of an organisation, devising and administering selection procedures for jobs, and developing training and retraining programmes for the workforce. This work would also involve the design and provision of job aids, in the form of instruction, troubleshooting procedures, and training manuals.

Management services. This function can cover a variety of tasks, including operational research, planning, production and office system design, and marketing. Ergonomists are often to be found working in these areas, in response to the growing recognition that many, if not all, planning and system design decisions will eventually affect the welfare, satisfaction, and performance of people. An important example of activities such as these is the introduction of computers and related devices into office and factory environments, with the attendant problems of job design, and individual performance with new technology. This will involve not only the specification of workplace design and environmental conditions in the workplace, but also the design of user–computer dialogues and that of the most appropriate computer hardware for the job.

As hinted above, ergonomists also work as independent consultants or researchers, advising companies, government departments, the armed services, and other institutions. Their work may be in the applied area, solving immediate practical problems in equipment design, operational procedures, and the implementation of technology; or it may be at a more basic level, involving research into the physical, perceptual, and cognitive characteristics of Man. Research and consultancy organisations may be established as independent companies or as part of a department in a university or other educational establishment.

Further reading

BAILEY, R.W. (1982). *Human performance engineering: a guide for system designers*. London: Prentice-Hall

DAMODARAN, L., SIMPSON, A., and WILSON, P. (1980). *Designing systems for people*. Manchester: NCC Publications

GRANDJEAN, E. (1981). *Fitting the task to the man*. London: Taylor and Francis

HUTCHINSON, R.D. (1981). *New horizons for human factors in design*. New York: McGraw-Hill

KVALSETH, T.O. (1983). *Ergonomics of workstation design*. London: Butterworth

McCORMICK, E.J. and SANDERS, M.S. (1982). *Human factors in engineering and design*, 5th edn. New York: McGraw-Hill

MURRELL, H. (1975). *Men and machines*. London: Methuen

OBORNE, D.J. (1982). *Ergonomics at work*. New York: Wiley

VAN COTT, H.P. and KINKADE, R.G. (1972). *Human engineering guide to equipment design*. US Govt. Printing Office

WEINER, J.S. and MAULE, H.G. (1977) *Case studies in ergonomics practice, 1: Human factors in work design and production*. London: Taylor and Francis

Chapter 2

Approaches and models in ergonomics

In this chapter we consider the points in the development of a product or facility at which the ergonomist's contribution can be made, and the various ways in which ergonomics problems are approached and analysed.

How and where ergonomics is used

Many people might have a reasonable idea of the need to use ergonomics principles and data in the design and manufacture of equipment, domestic products, facilities, environments, and operating procedures. At the same time, there is often some confusion in knowing at what stage, in the process of design, development, and manufacture, ergonomics information should be used. For example, should an industrial designer go as far as making a three-dimensional model of the product before calling on the ergonomist for 'fine-tuning' of the design? Should the designer of a computer system install the system in an organisation and call in the ergonomist to evaluate it and to make suggestions as to how the system should be modified? Or should ergonomics be involved at earlier stages of both these examples?

Ideally, ergonomics should be used in design and development programmes from their inception. As indicated in the previous chapter, ergonomics involves specifying design with the requirements of the user as the starting point and as the main criterion for effectiveness. A system whose main design criterion is something other than this—say engineering convenience—is going to be very difficult to change halfway through its development, and it will be very expensive to do so. Making changes to prototype systems or even finished and manufactured products may involve the re-tooling of manufacturing machines, and changes in manufacturing procedures, and even then the extent to which this can be done may be limited. Thus the ergonomist is called upon at a stage in the process that is too late for the most effective use to be made of his or her skills and knowledge.

In the light of this, it is worth considering where, in the design, development, and production process, ergonomics can and should be used. Although this discussion is set largely in the context of product and equipment design, the same arguments can be applied easily to the design of environments, working procedures, and any other application area of the subject.

Stage 1: Identifying the client's needs

Many potential clients will know enough about ergonomics to wish to use ergonomics information and advice, but are unfamiliar with the ergonomics approach. More specifically, there is often some uncertainty as to what questions should be put to an ergonomist, and at what stage. In some cases, there is some doubt as to what the ergonomics problems might be, or even in what stage of product design and development they might lie. In other words, the client suspects that an ergonomics problem might exist, but doesn't know where it is or what questions to ask in order to identify it. By working with the client at this very early stage, the ergonomist can help to identify the important ergonomics issues. The ergonomist will seek to understand the aims of the design and development project, and will discuss with the client the proposed features of the product, its anticipated mode of use, and the people who are expected to use it. Areas in which problems may arise in manufacture and use will be identified in this discussion. The consultation may end at that point if the client so wishes, or if the potential ergonomics problems turn out to be illusory. However, the important thing is that the investigation has been made. This stage can be called 'problem identification'—it is the crucial first step in any ergonomics programme.

Example. A County Education Department in England had received reports of general concern from school teachers about the welfare of school children in respect of the furniture and equipment used in the schools. The problem was poorly defined at that stage because, although the Education Department appreciated that ergonomics might help in solving this problem, it did not fully know how to identify the problem areas. The initial stage of the project was therefore a discussion with representatives of the Education Department and with school teachers, in which their concerns could be 'translated' into issues amenable to ergonomics analysis. This stage functioned both as a clarification of the problem and as an education of the teachers and others so that they could return to their schools and review their concerns in the light of what they then knew about ergonomics.

Stage 2: Identifying the user's needs

If a product is to be successful in the market it must appeal to the purchaser and must fulfil needs that are not met by other products. Implicit in this is the fact that the product must perform according to the user's requirements. The size of a market is largely a question for the market researcher, as is that of the emotional appeal of the product. However, ergonomics skills are needed in order to establish in detail the functional requirements of the user, to investigate systematically how and under what circumstances existing products are used, and to provide a blueprint of the functional characteristics of the proposed product. Identifying what the user requires, and how the user copes with existing devices, is not necessarily a simple matter of question and answer; this is because many people take their use of products and services for granted, without thinking in detail about the way in which usage takes place. Indeed, there is no reason why people should think in such a detailed fashion: the office worker will want to switch on his or her computer, and get on with the job of entering text, making forecasts of monthly sales, and so on; the user of a domestic cooker will be concerned with producing food that is hot and cooked, but not burned. In both these cases, the details of the operations necessary to achieve the goals (correct forecasts, good food) will be of passing and superficial interest and will only be noticed if some significant problem occurs. Minor inconvenience on a few occasions may not be remembered, even though it may be of interest in having long-term implications. The ergonomist, by a process of close questioning, observation, and measurement, will be able to guide the user through the sequence of tasks, and will deduce the requirements of the user from this process. This stage of the ergonomist's work can be called 'concept identification'.

Example. A manufacturer of circular saws for the domestic market will want to identify those features of a saw which are important to the user and which determine or affect the way in which the saw is used. An ergonomist would set up a trial in which a sample of users are presented with a range of existing saws, which are each used for a set number of tasks. On the basis of pilot studies, the ergonomist will observe and question the user in relation to a number of features of the saw and its operation, such as handle design, weight, cutting efficiency, noise and vibration, possibility of abuse, ease of cleaning and maintenance, and other factors. The user can say whether one saw is better or worse than another in any of these respects. The result of this exercise will be a list of desirable and undesirable features of the saw, and an indication of their relative importance to the user. Such information can guide the designer and manufacturer because it reflects the user's requirements in respect of the functional characteristics of the product, and will furnish a list of priorities for the eventual design.

Stage 3: Contributing design data

Once the functional characteristics of the product have been specified, it is necessary to produce a technical specification which will enable a physical object to be manufactured. At this stage, the ergonomist will work with the industrial designer or design engineer, and will provide data about human characteristics and their variability in the population of potential users. The data will relate to physical characteristics of people, such as their size, weight, and strength; to perceptual features, such as the ability to see and hear; to cognitive features, such as the speed with which people can process information, or their ability to understand messages; to motor features, such as the rate at which a control can be used, or the accuracy with which it can be set; and to biological features, such as the body's ability to adapt to hot or cold environments, and the effect that this adaptation can have on performance. The data themselves can refer to adults, children, the elderly and disabled, or any of a range of user groups. This process is perhaps closest to the image of what an ergonomist does but, as can be seen, it is not the ergonomist's only task. It can be described as 'product creation'.

Example. Ergonomists contributed to the design of a computer system that was to be used for the collection and analysis of data about patients in a hospital ward. An important part of this was the design of the computer terminal—the keyboard and display unit that would reside in the ward and which would be used by clinicians many times a day. Based on a projection of the position in which the unit would be used, ergonomics data were used to specify the size, shape, and angle of the keyboard and its keys, and the size and orientation of the display. Knowledge of the clinicians' keyboard skills determined the function of each of the keys; information about the data to be entered determined how the keys were to be grouped and how they were to be colour coded; knowledge of the circumstances in which data would be entered helped to decide the design of the computer programme which controlled this. In all, the computer system was designed to fit the physical and cognitive characteristics of the users, the circumstances in which they worked, their requirements for training, and the needs of the ward and the hospital as a whole. Without the ergonomics data it is very unlikely that the computer system would have been acceptable to the user.

Stage 4: Evaluating the product

Designing a product or facility always involves a number of assumptions. These concern the characteristics of the user, the circumstances of use and abuse, the relevance of data used in the design, and the accuracy of the functional specification. In addition, any design is a compromise between a number of criteria, which sometimes will conflict: for example, a product which is very safe may be very expensive; one which is simple to manufacture may not be reliable. The end result may compromise one of these criteria to an unacceptable extent. However, without these assumptions and compromises, design could not proceed, but they must always be checked once the design has been materialised. This checking is done by means of a formal evaluation.

Evaluations can take place at various stages in the creation of a product, and can vary in complexity and sophistication. A simple evaluation may involve a group of users commenting on a drawing of the product in a fairly informal manner; a sophisticated one may involve large numbers of users each using the product for a considerable length of time, and detailed measures of their performance being taken. The evaluation may be made on a mockup of the product relatively early in the design process, on a fully working prototype further on in the process, or on an already marketed product. Evaluations may be made of the product as a whole, or of only a part of it. The essence of any evaluation, however, is that it is a reliable and valid trial, based on scientific principles, which will yield accurate answers. The measures taken can be physical, psychological, social, biological, or a combination of these. The results should indicate clearly in what respects

the product is successful or deficient in meeting the needs and characteristics of the user, and will provide feedback to the designer and manufacturer so that the product can be improved. This form of evaluation will
often complement those made by other specialists: an engineering evaluation will provide data concerning physical integrity and quality, whilst an
economic one will indicate the degree of market success and profitability.
This last stage can be called 'product evaluation'.

Example. A vehicle manufacturer had produced several alternatives for
the design of a car instrument panel. These were subjected to ergonomics
evaluation in a series of experiments of increasing sophistication, ranging
from the presentation, under laboratory conditions, of projector slides of
the designs, through to the installation of working prototypes into actual
vehicles, and the conduct of trials on the public roads. The measures taken
were the accuracy with which the instruments could be read, and user
preference for each of the designs. Both accuracy and preference were
measured in a number of ways. The evaluation led to the incorporation of
some of the designs into production vehicles, and it generated useful data
about the way in which instruments of this type are actually used.

Models and approaches in ergonomics

In carrying out the four stages discussed above, the ergonomist uses a basic
conceptualisation of people and the tasks they carry out, as well as a formal
approach to the analysis and design of user–machine systems. These are
discussed below.

The most general approach to ergonomics is to think of a person
interacting with a machine (Fig 2.1). This interaction is made by means of
displays by which the machine passes information to the user, and controls
by which the user passes information to the machine. There is thus a
complete information flow loop, all parts of which must function properly
and which must not cause any delays in the flow of information if successful, safe, and efficient use is to be achieved.

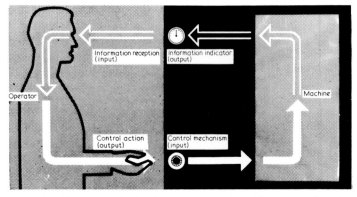

Figure 2.1 The communication between user and machine can be viewed as an information
flow loop connecting their respective inputs and outputs.

Looked at in this way, the human being is a device which receives information and which takes action; within the device is a mechanism which makes decisions, and which thus links the information entering with that leaving the device. Even such a crude model of the human can be useful: the separation of perceptual (input), cognitive (mediation), and motor (output) functions would suggest whether a proposed solution to a user–machine problem is likely to work. This is because a solution which addresses, say, the perceptual function is not going to be successful if the problem is a cognitive one. For example, making the symbols on a road sign larger or more distinct (a perceptual approach) will not improve the sign if the basic problem is one of understanding what the symbol means (a cognitive problem).

This simple model can be elaborated in order to answer a number of questions. For example, how does human memory affect decision making? Is memory a single mechanism or a set of different mechanisms? How are attitudes and opinions formed, and what is their effect? Why are people able to concentrate on one thing, and ignore others? Are we able to process more than one item of information simultaneously? What determines our interest in some things, and apathy towards others? Much work has been carried out to investigate these and other questions, and there is general agreement on some, and disagreement on others. A discussion of these issues is beyond the scope of this book; references given at the end of this chapter will guide the interested reader.

Tasks, however, are not carried out in a vacuum. In all cases, the interaction between user and machine takes place within some workspace, which itself is located in an environment (Fig 2.2). The characteristics of the workspace and the environment will affect the performance of the task. The workspace is described in terms of the size and layout of chairs, tables and desks, consoles, gangways, and other equipment. These will affect the

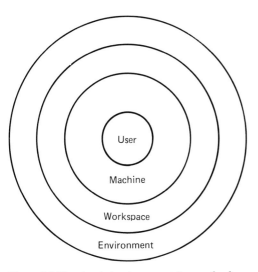

Figure 2.2 The simple but important frame of reference and orientation needed.

position, posture, and reach of the expected range of users, and hence their comfort and efficiency. Workspace design is discussed in Chapter 6. The environment may be described in physical terms, such as climate, lighting, noise and vibration, and the presence and effect of chemical and biological agents; and in psychological terms, such as workteam and command structure, shift conditions, psychosociological factors, and so forth. Specific chapters later in this book discuss some environmental factors.

The user–machine–workspace–environment model is useful in emphasising the influences on task performance, and, if used consistently, ensures that no potential ergonomics factor will be ignored. However, it is primarily a descriptive device, and does not offer much direction as to how and in what order a system should be analysed or designed. To do this, but bearing the model in mind, we may consider a formal method of analysis which has been used successfully in a very large number of ergonomics investigations. It is known as the systems approach.

The systems approach

As stressed above, the object for which any user–machine system is designed will be achieved only if all its components are matched to each other and interact in ways appropriate to their common purpose. The properties and performance of each component can be properly assessed only in the context of the system. A car speedometer which will serve its purpose for twenty years might be thought to be better than one which will do so for only five, but as a component of a low-priced car which is itself designed to last for only five years the second instrument will be better since it will be cheaper. Again, there can be no intrinsically 'best' seat: the best for the crane operator will certainly not be so for the television viewer. The need to assess components in their relationship to the systems of which they are a part applies no less to human components than it does to the mechanical components which they use.

Systems design differs from engineering design in the importance it attaches to the human operator as an integral part of the system to be designed, and in the emphasis it lays on the suitability of all components for the functions to be allocated to them for the achievement of the overall purpose. This broader concept of the task, the growing complexity of equipment, the mounting cost of design errors, and the need to develop new systems quickly all combine to demand a critical examination of the design and analysis process itself. The success of the systems approach to design depends on the close collaboration of the designer, the engineer, and the ergonomist.

Aspects of the systems design process

The logical approach to the design task is to break it down into a pattern of decisions which lays due emphasis on the complementary engineering and human factors, and which is applicable in principle to all systems design problems. This process, as outlined in Fig 2.3, may appear simple but will seldom prove so in practice: each of the many variables is likely to

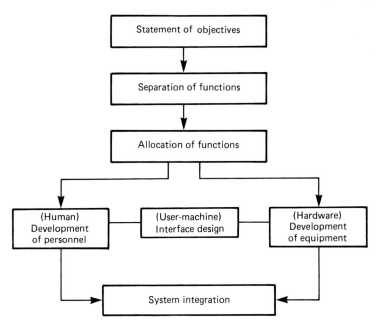

Figure 2.3 The systems design process.

influence others, and decisions concerning the allocation of functions, interface design (ie the design of the connecting links), and training all interact to an extent which makes it necessary for the systems designer to evaluate many alternatives before reaching the final decision.

Allowance has often to be made for a number of conflicting requirements, and in the more complex cases it can be virtually impossible for the designer to envisage and evaluate the many alternative patterns which can result from the permutation of the possible solutions of the problems which occur. For this reason, research is being undertaken into methods of increasing peoples' capacity to evaluate alternatives, by the use of computers and other aids in the designing of new systems.

Statement of objectives
The purpose of a system is to accept certain inputs and transform them into the required outputs. The ranges of acceptable inputs and required outputs, together with their time relationships, form a statement of the objectives of the system.

Even at this stage, compromises are already being made with engineering feasibility, cost and user requirements. Stating objectives may appear to be a straightforward logical exercise, but it entails a very complex, essentially political set of decisions; this is why, in an industrial company, objectives are set by high-level committees. This, of course, does not excuse needless vagueness; and the insistence on a specification, as for example in Fig 2.4, can help to exert a necessary discipline. There are always some aspects of the specification, eg aesthetic considerations, which

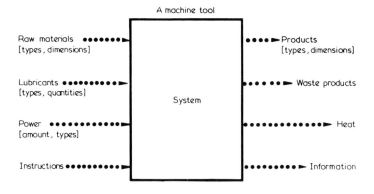

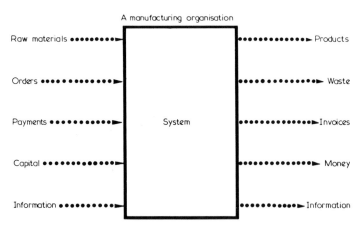

Figure 2.4 Statement of objectives. The top diagram shows all the inputs and outputs to a machine tool. The designer must know or estimate all of these factors, and the system should be the compromise best able to maximise the most wanted feature or features. For example, high versatility (many products) may be at the expense of high power requirement or high waste figures, and the best compromise must be achieved. The system can be much more complicated: for example, a manufacturing organisation, as shown in the bottom diagram. Here, the good manager still tries to maximise certain factors, eg money, with fixed orders and capital.

cannot be stated numerically, but, fortunately, these can be conveyed by verbal descriptions.

Separation of functions
The systems designer must think in terms of functions; in terms, that is, of the activities required to meet the objectives, as opposed to the ways in which they are to be effected by components. This ability is valuable in dealing with relatively straightforward systems, and becomes essential as they grow in complexity. For example, where power is required, the amount necessary is initially more important than the means of obtaining it; diesel engines and electric motors are physical devices for transducing

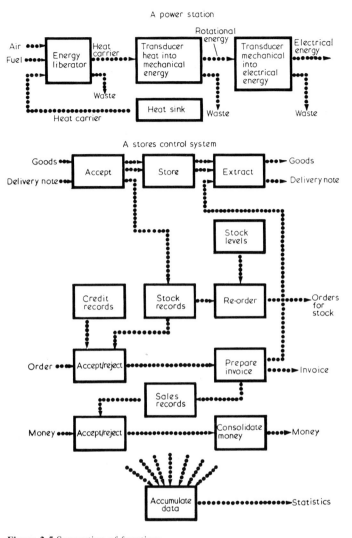

Figure 2.5 Separation of functions.

energy, and in designing a system the decision as to which should be used is best left for later consideration.

Perhaps most important of all, initial analysis into functions simplifies subsequent decisions as to what the activities of the human and mechanical components in the system shall be. Fig 2.5 shows two illustrations of this separation of functions at a gross level. These would need to be further subdivided before the 'allocation of functions' could be made.

Allocation of functions
It may be helpful at this point to trace the historical development of this approach to the problem of allocating functions between human and

Table 2.1 Fitts list: relative advantages of men and machines

	Machine	*Man*
Speed	Much superior.	Lag 1 second.
Power	Consistent at any level. Large, constant standard forces.	2.0 hp for about 10 s 0.5 hp for a few minutes 0.2 hp for continuous work over a day
Consistency	Ideal for: routine; repetition; precision.	Not reliable; should be monitored by machine.
Complex activities	Multi-channel.	Single-channel.
Memory	Best for literal reproduction and short-term storage.	Large store, multiple access. Better for principles and strategies.
Reasoning	Good deductive.	Good inductive.
Computation	Fast, accurate. Poor at error correction.	Slow, subject to error. Good at error correction.
Input sensitivity	Some outside human senses, eg radioactivity.	Wide energy range (10^{12}) and variety of stimuli dealt with by one unit; eg eye deals with relative location, movement and colour. Good at pattern detection. Can detect signals in high noise levels.
	Can be designed to be insensitive to extraneous stimuli.	Affected by heat, cold, noise and vibration (exceeding known limits).
Overload reliability	Sudden breakdown.	'Graceful degradation.'
Intelligence	None.	Can deal with unpredicted and unpredictable; can anticipate.
Manipulative abilities	Specific.	Great versatility.

mechanical components. Until about 1950, military design was pursued in terms of simple on-line competition with the enemy, and the criteria for allocation of functions were based on the relative abilities of men and machines. This thinking was the origin of the *Fitts List* (produced by Paul Fitts, late Director of the Human Performance Centre, University of Michigan) illustrated in Table 2.1. It may be noted here that, although the relative capacities of men and machine are apparent in broad outline, as indicated in this list, more research may be necessary in order to express them in quantitative terms; the designer has often to resort to experiment to determine these factors in a particular system.

After 1950, the complexity of weapons systems increased to the point where cost became of critical importance, even to the larger nations, and a new criterion—the cost/value function—was added as a measure of the relative cost and effectiveness of performing functions with human operators or mechanical equipment. When these concepts spread into the field of industry, in about 1960, two further criteria were added. The first was the need for integrated tasks—that is, tasks which adequately utilise the abilities of human operators, and, at the same time, make allowance for their limitations. The second was the need in large systems for graded tasks matched to the differing levels of ability and seniority to be found in every population. The whole philosophy underlying the allocation of functions is now increasingly centred on the human operator.

Personnel aspects of system design

Development of personnel
All the personnel decisions must be made in relation to the three main phases of activity with which human operators will be concerned: setting up the system, operating it, and providing the maintenance it will inevitably require. It may be noted that, although in so-called 'automatic' systems the operator is not employed on-line, people are still needed for the other activities; there is no basis in fact for the common assumption that all human factor problems can be eliminated by designing automatic devices.

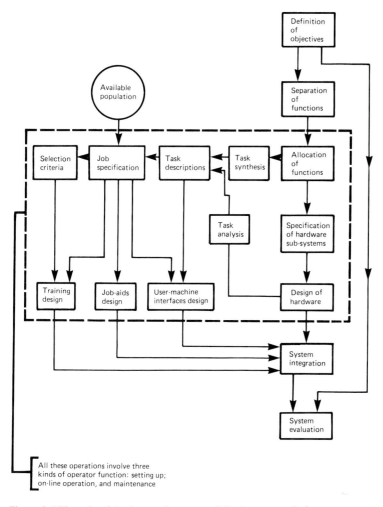

Figure 2.6 The role of the human factors specialist in systems design.

The extent of the field covered by the human factors specialist in systems design is shown in Fig 2.6.

The task description
The basis, and first step, of all human factors work is the task description—that is, a simple statement of the functions which have been allocated to human operators. In the case of the design of new systems, this can be done at the initial stage by logically determining the job of individual operators from the demands of the system. In systems already in operation, the task descriptions are determined by observing and measuring what the operators in fact do.

The function of task description in co-ordinating the human factors information required in the systems analysis is outlined in Fig 2.7.

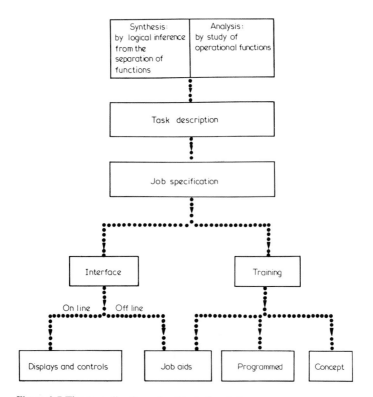

Figure 2.7 The co-ordinating role of task description.

The job specification
The next step is to build up job specifications; that is, to determine how many operators will be required, what skills they must have to achieve the system's objectives, which of these skills are to be obtained by selection and which by training, and how the selection and training are to be effected.

Interface design

If machine and user are to be matched to form an integral working unit, close attention must be paid to the area of contact between them—the display and control interface—in order to reconcile their fundamentally different characteristics. The design of the one and the skills of the other must be such that the information output of the machine is adapted to the receptive intake of the user, and the physical output of the user to the control requirements of the machine. The number of variables involved makes this a difficult area of investigation, and there is no unique series of decisions which will lead to a solution; one of the arts of interface design is the consideration, in an order which suits the particular case, of all the variable factors as shown in Fig 2.8.

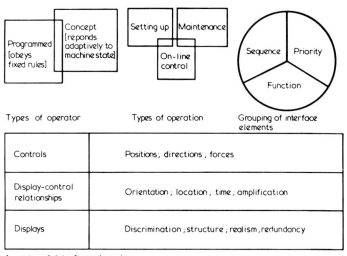

Figure 2.8 Interface design decision matrix.

An interface design for a 'programmed' operator, that is the operator who has only to obey rules (for example, to press a switch when a pointer reading reaches a stated value, without knowing what the reading represents or what the switch does) will differ from the interface required for a 'concept' operator, that is the operator who understands the system and can decide the control action appropriate to the interpretation of the machine state. Programmed operators are used considerably in modern systems, and, although setting up and maintenance operations are now undertaken mainly by concept operators, there is a trend towards making maintenance a programmed operation (eg 'When red lamp lights up, replace component No. 74').

There must be a pattern in both the operator's search for information from the machine displays and the responses to what they say. This can be established by reference to the sequence of operations (where this is fixed), the relative priorities of different display and control elements (as measured by either frequency of use or consequences of omission), and the functional aspects of the equipment (eg control of power or position). All these factors will influence the details of interface elements, including their positioning in relation to each other and the operator, the accuracy of the readings required, and the levels of force necessary. Interface design demands far more than the provision of dials to suit the operator's eyes and of controls convenient for the limbs. The most superficial study will show that sense organs and muscles have their limitations, for which allowance must be made, but it is not so obvious that between sense organs and muscles there are computing devices which perform certain functions. It is these computing devices which give rise to the critical interface design problems. The presentation of the necessary data should require of the operator the minimum of thought and computation ('encoding'), and should guide the operator towards the correct decisions. This calls for consideration of the way in which the given information will be organised in order to reach decisions, and requires that the data shall be organised as far as possible before it is presented at the interface—which is in effect an allocation of function.

The problems of control dynamics are often mathematically complex in that they require a statement of the time-relationship between control movements and the resultant changes in the state of the system. Large systems may have considerable inertia, resulting in a significant time lag between changes in control settings and the appearance on displays of their full effects. The sometimes impossibly high degree of anticipatory skill such systems require can be reduced by the use of predictor displays.

The design of job aids
The instructions to be provided for the operator are another aspect of the interface problem, and close attention must be paid to the method of their presentation in relation to the information they are required to convey. Instructions may be given by legend plates on machines, by charts, diagrams or manuals, or computer-based training packages. The design of manuals and the like offers much scope for improvement (even in such basic aspects as the separation of setting up, on-line control and maintenance), and deserves more attention than it commonly receives. As shown in Fig 2.7, job aids comprise both training devices and interface elements.

Selection and training
The criteria for selecting and training operators are based on the job specification, and depend on the type of operator required, the complexity of the interface, and the availability of training facilities. Concept training, which is essentially education, will be necessary where the operator must understand the system sufficiently well to be able to interpret any development and formulate a method of dealing with the situation it indicates. Such training has little in common with that needed to enable an operator to learn a series of predetermined patterns of action in response to specific states of the system.

Conclusion
It is impossible either to assign hard and fast priorities to the various interacting factors which the systems designer must take into account, or to

specify the order in which the decisions relating to the allocation of functions, interface design and training should be made. The concepts described above are by no means fanciful, and nothing has been advocated which is not practised intuitively by the good designer. They derive from the fact that if the designer is to be successful in the solution of the range of problems which occur, either a high level of innate ability, or long experience or an understanding of the philosophy of systems design is needed. Marked natural ability is rare, and the rapid emergence of new technologies exacts a heavy penalty for mistakes which may be made while experience is being gained.

Systems design is therefore to be regarded as an educational and disciplinary procedure which encourages a logical and systematic approach to the problems of making design decisions. It does not provide the answers to the questions, but it does define what those questions should be, and it emphasises the fact that many of them relate to human beings.

Workstation analysis

Within the systems design framework are two further, and important, aspects of the ergonomics approach. These are known as workstation analysis, and evaluation. The importance of evaluation has already been stressed, and examples of it are to be found in other chapters of this book. Workstation analysis, however, is discussed in more detail here.

For each part of a system where a human element is used, the interaction between the person and the equipment must be optimised. The ergonomic approach at this level is to examine the task and the operational sequence which the person must follow, and then work outwards from this, considering the interaction firstly with the machine, next with the immediate workspace, and finally with the general environment in which the task is carried out.

This approach is applicable both to each of the separate workstations within any large system and to the consideration of single user–machine combinations. It can be used as an initial guide when studying new problems in an existing situation and when designing new workstations. It differs from traditional approaches to design in that it places the human (operator, supervisor, maintainer, controller, manager, etc) at the centre of the frame of reference, and works outwards to consider equipment, workspace, and environment, and the interactions between all of the elements.

The analysis proceeds through a series of questioning and definition steps, leading to a formal statement of the situation. This establishes the basis for the next stage, which will be a set of recommendations, initial design proposals, or a full design for evaluation. The sequence of the analysis is given in Table 2.2, and is discussed below. The sequence should not be treated as a set of independent units to be considered separately and once only. Some aspects and answers in the first two main areas (user and machine) inevitably interact. The analysis is likely to proceed through the various steps several times, and sometimes to cover aspects in two areas simultaneously. The process is iterative until all the information is gathered for each area, and then the marshalling and final consideration of it all is organised under the successive headings of the framework.

Table 2.2 Workstation analysis outline

User

Consideration of sex   physique   training
                  age   intelligence motivation
                  size   experience

Definition of operational modes, eg   searching   monitoring
                                       tracking   decision-taking

required in final situation and thus consideration of abilities and limitations of human operator for all aspects of the task.

User–machine interaction
Influence, on operator and decisions, of
              displays — sensory input to operator
              controls — motor output from operator
              panel layouts — display-control compatibility

based upon study of human information–decision–action patterns and of human, equipment, and task operational sequences.

User–workspace interaction
Influence, on operator's position, posture, and reach, of
              machine size
              chairs, desks, etc
              adjacent machines, structures and material etc.

User–environment interaction
Influence, upon behaviour and performance, of
              physical aspects
              chemical aspects
              biological aspects
              psychological aspects.

Physical: light and colour, noise, heat, ventilation, gravity, movement, electromagnetic and nuclear radiation.

Chemical: gas or liquid, composition, pressure, smell.

Biological: microbes, insects, animals.

Psychological: workteam, command structure, pay and welfare, shift conditions, discomfort or risk, socio-psychological aspects of the particular factory, neighbourhood, town, and type of industry concerned.

Special questions
Consideration of non-standard conditions, such as errors, exceptional circumstances, or similar factors not included in the previous analysis of normal operation. Consideration of problems peculiar to the specific case under investigation.

The user

The first step is to define the profiles of the likely range of people to use the workstation to be analysed. Important characteristics will include the range and limits of age, sex, body size, mobility, strength, intelligence, experience and training of the expected users. Emphasis will be placed on the range of any characteristic, rather than on its average value, because facilities designed for the average value are likely to be unsatisfactory for those at the extremes of the range. It is customary to attempt to accommodate at least 90% of the population within the design, although this may not always be feasible and compromises must be made.

Depending upon the situation being analysed, it may be possible to interview, study, and learn in other ways from those doing either the exact task or types of task similar to those envisaged. This exercise, although time-consuming, can be valuable, for the following reasons:

• Basic knowledge of the system is improved because the analyst has more data, particularly if those data are based on objective studies and detailed discussions with the task performers.
• Basic understanding is improved of what it is like to be the person whose task is being studied. This might be quite different from what one might suppose by doing the task oneself.
• Potential users become involved in the design exercise, and it consequently has a better chance of acceptance in the long run. This is particularly so if the project involves a specialised design or redesign for a specific installation and a small group of users.

The machine
The next step, which can be concurrent with the first, is to understand fully the operation of any machines involved, and the interaction of the user with them. Note that 'machine' includes any non-human aspect of the equipment or the task. Using the simple model of user–machine interaction described above, the information–decision–action sequences involving user and machine can be specified. An example of this is given in Table 2.3, taken from Mayall and Shackel (1961). It is not always necessary to prepare complete operational sequences, but their benefits in terms of the questions and problems revealed usually repay amply the cost of the time needed to complete them.

From the information–decision–action concept one is reminded to ask, for each sequence, whether the user receives all the information needed for the decision to be made, and whether it is presented adequately by the displays; whether the decision can be signalled easily and effectively or whether better controls are required; and whether displays and controls are compatible with each other and are located appropriately by good panel and machine layout. Thus the convenient division of the operator into sensory input, decision making, and motor output sections is usefully matched by the division of the machine into displays, controls, and panel and machine layouts. This equipment-oriented subdivision is often helpful both in organising the data and, when the analysis is finished, in considering it for design purposes.

Workspace
Moving outwards from the user–machine interaction, the interaction of the user with the immediate surrounding space is next considered. All factors are studied which may affect the position, posture, and reach of the expected range of users, and thus their comfort and efficiency. This will include tables, chairs, machines, consoles, work in progress, and spaces for movement. In developing a design, further detailed studies are made. For instance, following an analysis and design on the drawing board, using tabulated anthropometric data, mockups of the proposed design are made and are evaluated in a formal trial, with samples of the expected user

Table 2.3 General analysis of bench drill operation and detailed operational sequence of the 'Drill' section

General analysis	Detailed operational sequence of the 'Drill' section State at start: drill mounted and depth set; drill speed set; workpiece mounted, centred and clamped	
	Operational sequence	Notes of questions to be checked as design progresses
Sections of job	Final check of drawing	Where will the drawing be?
PRELIMINARIES	→ Final check drill suitability, size, depth setting and machine speed setting	Can operator easily see and measure drill size, depth setting and machine speed?
Receive drawings and instructions. Get materials and tools	→ Check safety guards in place	Are guards *really easy* to put on? Check with safety officer?
Mark off and punch workpiece	→ Switch on machine	Which hand? Easy to reach? Emergency off even easier?
MAN-MACHINE TASK	→ Supply lubricant	Which hand? Where is lubricant stored?
Mount workpiece	→ Grasp operating lever Lower drill	Which hand? Easy to do? Position comfortable? Control good? Gear ratio, etc – refer to ergonomic data?
Mount drill	→ Drill tip touches and dimples material	Lighting good enough? Need light on the machine?
Set drill depth	→ Raise drill	
Set drill speed	→ Check position of dimple with punch mark	Lighting good enough?
Centre workpiece	→ Lubricate	
Drill ↓	→ Lower drill	
Check hole depth		

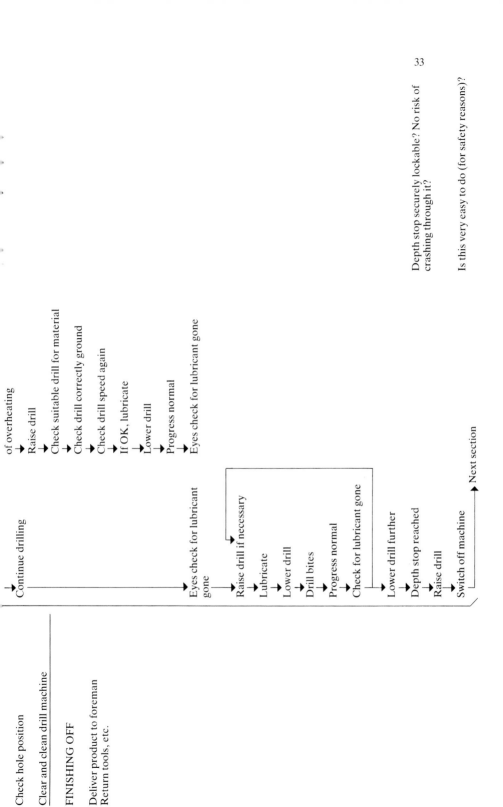

Check hole position

Clear and clean drill machine

FINISHING OFF

Deliver product to foreman
Return tools, etc.

Continue drilling

Eyes check for lubricant gone

Raise drill if necessary → Lubricate → Lower drill → Drill bites → Progress normal → Check for lubricant gone → Lower drill further → Depth stop reached → Raise drill → Switch off machine

→ Next section

of overheating → Raise drill → Check suitable drill for material → Check drill correctly ground → Check drill speed again → If OK, lubricate → Lower drill → Progress normal → Eyes check for lubricant gone

Depth stop securely lockable? No risk of crashing through it?

Is this very easy to do (for safety reasons)?

population. More recently, much of the cost, uncertainty, and inconvenience of trials with mockups has been eliminated by the development of computer-aided design facilities where alternative solutions can be set up, manipulated, and evaluated for fit. More information about this aspect of workstation analysis is given in Chapter 6.

Environment
Moving outwards again, the interaction between the user and the general environment is considered. The interaction is considered in both physical and psychological terms. The measured characteristics of the actual environment under study, or the expected or specified characteristics of the new design, are first detailed and compared with published ergonomics data about human performance under various environmental conditions. These data are discussed in more detail in Chapters 7, 8 and 9.

Poor environmental conditions are often to be found in practice. In control rooms and offices housing computer equipment, for instance, lighting levels and the position of lighting units are often such as to interfere seriously with the efficient performance of tasks. In daylight, glare from windows can cause discomfort and inefficiency, and the light may be reflected off screens and instruments, making them difficult or impossible to read. Shadows from natural or artificial light can be as troublesome as the light itself. On factory floors, in road vehicles, and in engine rooms, noise and vibration, unless properly controlled, can be unsafe as well as distracting. In the home as well as in the office or factory, poor climatic control (temperature, humidity, and ventilation) will have effects on a large number of tasks.

It is often very difficult to change environmental conditions unless the designer is responsible for a complete installation, including the equipment, the workspace, and the environment as an integrated unit. This is unusual; however, it does not mean that nothing can be done. For small pieces of equipment, the manufacturer can give advice to users about unsuitable environmental conditions, and the designer can often allow for known working conditions. For instance, the intensities of warning lights and sounds can be specified for most conditions of lighting and noise, and reflections from VDU screens can be reduced by allowing the user to move the screen, or by supplying non-reflective overlays for the screen. Controls may be similarly modified to suit the expected environmental conditions: those expected to be used in cold conditions can be designed to be large enough for operation by a gloved, rather than a bare hand; and for humid climates the control could have a textured surface which is resistant to slippage when used by damp fingers.

Special questions
The analysis outlined under the previous headings tends to address normal conditions and regular, routine procedures. Special questions, however, study what might go wrong, what errors and exceptional circumstances might arise, what procedures and sequences are non-regular (for instance, maintenance or repair), and what emergency conditions and procedures are needed. The essential questions asked here are of the type 'What happens if . . .?', and the aim is to identify all the unusual events that might arise, and make suitable provision for them.

An example of typical results from this section of the analysis, as from other parts, is given in Shackel (1969).

Conclusions on the workstation analysis
The importance of the approach recommended in this framework and formal analysis depends on three things, as follows.

First, this concept is problem-oriented rather than discipline-oriented: the categories and subdivisions are cast in terms of practical problem areas as they are met in the applied field, rather than in terms of the scientific disciplines from which knowledge may be drawn. This problem-oriented approach is desirable to ensure that all the relevant scientific knowledge for any given problem is brought to bear on it, irrespective of whether that knowledge is based on physics, biology, chemistry, psychology, or any other of a range of areas.

Second, the approach, if followed with reasonable care, ensures comprehensive gathering of all relevant data about the problem. This diminishes the risk of wasted time and inadequate solutions caused by premature concentration on the apparent and not the real cause of the problem.

Third, it emphasises that tasks and the circumstances in which they are performed are dynamic. Therefore, any problem-solving approach must itself be dynamic: it must view the issue as a series of actions and interactions, with their own implications for subsequent task components. The study of operational sequences provides the basis for such a dynamic analysis.

Caveat on systems and workstation analyses

Both the workstation analysis and the larger systems analysis in which it can lie present the designer and ergonomist with a series of stages, steps, and questions. The advantages of this are

- a logical and systematic study of the problem,
- maximisation of the chances that important and relevant data are gathered, and minimisation of the chances of missing any,
- assistance with the decision process, for instance in establishing, modifying, and checking the achievement of performance goals and specifications.

The data and background information thus gathered clarify the problem in detail for the designer, preparing the way for the development and assessment of ideas. Thus, systems and workstation analysis, used as a checklist, can help with two of the four basic parts of the creative process:

- *preparation* by studying the problem in detail and defining the design aims;
- *incubation* by mulling over all the problem details so as to be completely familiar with them;
- *innovation* when the new ideas and solutions are created;
- *evaluation* when the new solutions are tested to find the best fit to all the requirements of the problem.

It is clearly the first and last of these stages which can be most aided by logical study and analysis, via systems and workstation analysis.

At the same time, these analyses have their limitations: they will not lead inexorably to a new or useful solution, and cannot replace creativity and innovation. Furthermore, specific problems may require a modification of the principles outlined, and thus the steps taken in the analyses should not be regarded as being 'carved in stone'. They should be used as an initial guide, and not much more.

The related suggestion is that each engineer, designer, or manager who intends to do something about the ergonomics aspects of a problem or project should at the very beginning develop and specify in detail the system and workstation analysis peculiar to that problem, using the general principles described above as a guide. The analysis will indicate also those points at which specialist advice will be required, whether from the engineer, ergonomist, health and safety specialist, or other disciplines.

Further reading

BAILEY, R.W. (1982). *Human performance engineering: a guide for system designers.* New Jersey: Prentice-Hall

BEISHON, J. and PETERS, G. (eds) (1981). *Systems behaviour*, 3rd edn. London: Harper and Row

DAMODARAN, L., SIMPSON, A., and WILSON, P. (1980). *Designing systems for people.* Manchester: NCC Publications

DE GREENE, K.B. (1970). *Systems psychology.* New York: McGraw-Hill

MAYALL, W.H. ånd SHACKEL, B. (1961). 'The control loop concept', *Design*, **148**, 42–48

SHACKEL, B. (1969). 'Workstation analysis—turning cartons by hand', *Applied Ergonomics*, **1**. 1, 45–51

SINGLETON, W.T., EASTERBY, R.S., and WHITFIELD, D. (eds) (1967). *The human operator in complex systems.* London: Taylor and Francis

WICKENS, C. (1984). *Engineering psychology and human performance.* Columbus, Ohio: Merrill

Chapter 3

The design of displays

Information flow from a machine is essential if the user is to make efficient use of that machine. In this chapter various forms of information display are considered, including auditory and visual qualitative displays, analogue and digital quantitative displays, and representational displays.

People using machines need information. The aircraft pilot needs to know how the engines are behaving, the factory worker has to monitor the state of manufacturing machines, the plant manager must keep track of all the variables in the process, and the maintenance engineer must make regular checks on even the most automatic device. So machines communicate with people, and the communication is two-way because the user often has to take some action on the basis of the information received, such as turning a knob or pressing a key.

The efficient operation of a machine depends on the ease of this two-way communication, and since the capacities of the human are limited, it is necessary to design the characteristics of the machine so as to fit those of the user. Thus, however ingeniously the relevant information is detected from the machine or process, the designer will not achieve complete success if the user has difficulty in reading or hearing the displays, or in operating the controls, and the information is not transmitted quickly and accurately. Some of the ergonomics principles relevant to the design of displays are given in this chapter; the design of controls and workstation layouts is discussed in Chapters 4 and 5.

The purpose of a display is to transmit information from machine to user in a manner appropriate to the system and task requirements. Functionally, a good display is one which allows the best combination of speed, accuracy, and sensitivity when transferring the necessary information from machine to user. This criterion of the 'best combination' cannot be defined absolutely; it depends upon the specific system under consideration. In some cases, speed is more important, in others accuracy (avoidance of error or ambiguity), and in others sensitivity (detection of the slightest change in the variable being displayed).

In order to meet the functional requirements of speed, accuracy and sensitivity, any display must satisfy three basic criteria. These criteria determine the final design and location of the display, and apply whether the display is visual, auditory, or employs any of the other senses. The three criteria are as follows.

Detection. A visual display must be visible, and an auditory display audible. There is little point in having a visual display that is obscured by other equipment (for instance, by the steering wheel in a car) or a warning sound that cannot be heard against the background noise. Whilst the requirement for detectability may be obvious, it is by no means met in the design of all equipment; neither are the solutions always obvious. For example, people with occupational hearing loss can only detect sounds in certain frequency bands. These should be used for audible warnings.

Recognition. After a display has been detected, it has to be read or listened to. It is perhaps this factor that has received the most attention from ergonomists and designers: the ergonomics literature abounds with data concerning the sizes of characters for visual displays, the contrast between figure and background, the type and level of illumination, the relative merits of fixed pointer and moving pointer dial displays, the trade-off between digital and analogue displays, and a host of other factors. Similar data can be found for the design of auditory displays, but less is available. All these data are intended to aid the designer to make displays that can be read (or heard) quickly and accurately. Speed of reading is particularly important in transport applications, because every second that the driver of a car spends looking at a display inside the vehicle is a second not spent looking at the most important visual display—the road ahead.

Understanding. It is not enough to design displays that are detectable and recognisable; their meaning must be clear as well. Barriers to under-standing can occur at two levels. First, the words and symbols used in the display may be too complicated for the user. For example, the words 'velocity' and 'coolant' may be less readily understood than 'speed' and 'water'. In general, words that are too long, uncommon, or technical will be understood less well than those that are short, common, and everyday. Abbreviations can sometimes shorten a long word or phrase effectively but they should be used with caution; the same applies when a word is replaced by a symbol, whether visual or auditory, because this is a form of abbreviation. At another level, however, understanding may be poor if the user has difficulty with the basic meaning of the data, and not just its labelling. For instance, although many motor cars have a visual display that shows the amount of charge to the battery, it is unlikely that a driver will make much sensible use of this display without a basic knowledge of electricity and the functions of a battery. Whilst it is possible to make a display more understandable by improving the language of its labels, there will be a limit to this, imposed by the basic knowledge of the user.

Before the details of a display are designed, the following information is needed:

(1) the type of technology to be used to present the information (visual/auditory, mechanical/electronic);
(2) the total range to be displayed of the variable about which information is to be presented;
(3) the maximum accuracy and sensitivity required in the transfer of information;
(4) the speed required in the transfer of information;

(5) the maximum equipment error of the unit about which information is to be transmitted (a detail often overlooked);
(6) the normal and the maximum distance between the display and the users of that display;
(7) the environment in which the display is to be used (illumination, noise, etc).

These data are needed, together with information about the system and task requirements, to decide first the general type of display which will be appropriate, and second the detailed design of the display.

Types of display

Displays, and the information they convey, may be divided into three broad types: qualitative, quantitative, and representational. It is usually best to choose the simplest type which can convey the required information efficiently. For example, many graduated gauges in cars, displaying oil pressure, water temperature, and other information, have been succeeded by warning lights, thus saving the driver the trouble of remembering the normal value, looking closely at the value displayed on the scale, and making a comparison between the two.

Each type of display is described separately below, together with an outline of the ergonomics design recommendations. Some examples of visual displays are shown in Fig 3.1.

Qualitative displays

These are suitable when the user needs to distinguish a small number of different conditions. In many industrial control centres, for example, qualitative displays are used to show whether valves are open or shut, generators on or off, and switches open or closed.

In general, a qualitative display will show broad states of a system; the state may be a simplification of some numerical range (such as cold, normal, and hot, rather than an exact temperature reading) or may be purely qualitative (such as the stop, caution, and go signals of a traffic light).

Design recommendations
The main requirement is that the indicators for each of the conditions should be as distinctive as possible.

Auditory indicators such as bells and buzzers are suitable for conditions where the presence or absence of a noise is sufficient; that is, no noise means 'normal', and noise means 'warning'. Alternatively, the change in the tone of a noise may convey the information. Unless a speech communication system is employed, very little additional information can be provided. The main advantage of auditory indicators is their ability to attract immediate attention from any direction—an important feature for warnings.

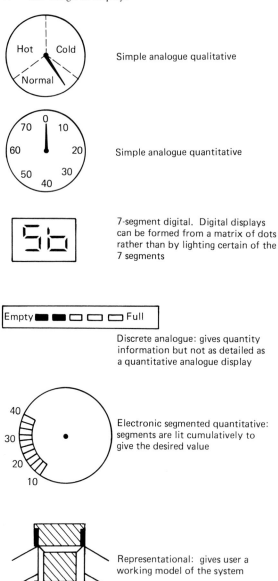

Simple analogue qualitative

Simple analogue quantitative

7-segment digital. Digital displays
can be formed from a matrix of dots
rather than by lighting certain of the
7 segments

Discrete analogue: gives quantity
information but not as detailed as
a quantitative analogue display

Electronic segmented quantitative:
segments are lit cumulatively to
give the desired value

Representational: gives user a
working model of the system

Figure 3.1 Types of visual display.

Visual indicators are essential for representing three or more conditions,
because they can be made distinctive through differences in position,
colour, shape and size. It is advisable to employ more than one of these
means, because the designer cannot rely on all the users being able to
distinguish the codes; for instance, it is estimated that some 10% of the

male population has difficulty in distinguishing red from green. A display that relied solely on a colour difference of this sort to differentiate two states could be misinterpreted.

Very important visual displays, such as warning devices, can be made more effective by the use of flashing lights, or by combining visual displays and audible warnings.

Quantitative displays

These are essential where the user requires numerical information from the system. The information can be presented usually in digital or analogue form for visual displays, or as speech communication for auditory displays.

Analogue indicators are so called because the position of a pointer on a scale is analogous to the value it represents. An analogue indicator can additionally be used to convey qualitative information, as when a red portion of the scale indicates danger. Digital indicators present the information directly as a number, and can use electromechanical counters or electronically generated numbers.

Figure 3.2 Both the analogue and the digital instrument can show the same value, but the analogue is better for quick check-reading, whereas the digital makes precise reading easier. The analogue may be better for indicating changing conditions.

Each of these two forms has its own advantages and disadvantages, and the designer should relate these to the kind of information the user requires. If precise readings are required, digital indicators are more suitable. Compare the two voltmeters in Fig. 3.2; these can both show the same value. The analogue display is more difficult to read because the user has to estimate the position of the pointer between two graduations on the scale. If precise information is to be read quickly then the digital indicator

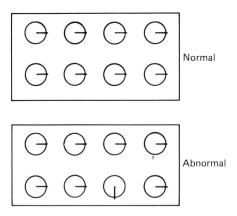

Figure 3.3 In a group of analogue visual displays, a deviant reading can be spotted easily if all the pointers are in the same direction under 'normal' conditions.

would be more suitable. For quick check reading, however, the analogue indicator would be better than the digital version, although large, simple digital indicators showing speed in a car are easier for check reading than many analogue designs. In general, the position of the pointer is easily checked, whereas the figures on poorly designed digital indicators may be misread (for instance, 368 may look similar to 386 at a glance). Rate and direction of change are shown much better by analogue indicators, although some electronic digital displays also can represent rate of change easily. Analogue displays are particularly useful when the states of a number of displays are to be shown together and deviations from the norm are to be noted (Fig. 3.3). Digital indicators are particularly helpful when the user must note precise readings in a log book, or input them into a computer.

Design recommendations
Analogue displays. There has been more research into the ergonomics features of electromechanical visual display design than of any other type of indicator. Detailed recommendations may be found in general ergonomics textbooks (see references at the end of the chapter) and so the scope of the available advice is merely mentioned here. Information on the design of electronic displays is also available, based mainly on VDU (visual display unit) technology. The performance criteria apply equally to electronic and electromechanical designs. However, the relationship between electronic displays and the environment in which they are used is much more critical than with electromechanical displays.

The aim should be to make the scale very legible. If possible, multiple scales on the same instrument, or non-linear scales, should be avoided. Simple recommendations on scale design cover the optimum length of scale and size of markings for various reading accuracies and viewing distances, number sequences, subdivisions, and the design of numerals.

To avoid reading errors, scales should be designed according to familiar conventions, so that numbering increases in a clockwise direction on a circular scale, upwards on a vertical straight scale, and to the right on a horizontal straight scale. Pointers should be of a simple shape and dials with many pointers should be avoided. It is well known that errors in interpreting multi-pointer altimeters have led to aircraft crashes. The update rate of discrete segmented movement on analogue electronic displays is critical for ease and accuracy of reading.

Digital displays. Here again, legibility is the designer's aim. The general ergonomics textbooks contain comprehensive recommendations for the dimensions, design, and colour of numerals, as well as the readability of various types of segmented electronic digital displays.

Representational displays

These provide the user with a 'working model' or 'mimic diagram' of the machine or process. They are most suitable for large remote control systems, as they enable the user to observe the functioning of each part in relation to the whole, and to locate faults or delays quickly.

Railway signal boxes are good examples of representational displays (Fig 3.4). Such displays are also to be found in many process industries; in cars, outline displays of the vehicle show the status of doors, lamps, bootlid, and bonnet (Fig 3.5).

Figure 3.4 A modern railway signal box in which the whole display gives the operator a useful 'picture' of the system. Specific indicators conveying special pieces of information, and the controls, are incorporated at appropriate points.

Design recommendations
The basic requirement is to make the display as simple in its logical scheme as possible. All irrelevant detail should be omitted; what is wanted is a representation of the critical components, not a complete simulation. The

Figure 3.5 A representational display showing the state of various components in a motor car. The image and legend on this display change as different states and conditions occur.

schematic map of the London underground railways is an excellent example: compared with the real geography all natural features except the river Thames are omitted, the lines are simplified into uncomplicated shapes, and the important central area is shown on a larger scale than the outlying parts (Fig 3.6).

The recommendations for both qualitative and quantitative displays will often be relevant as well. On the Underground map in Fig 3.6, each line has its own colour, and certain types of station are emphasised with distinctive symbols and lettering.

Colour in visual displays

Information can be visually coded by means of colour, brightness, shape, size, orientation, and other factors. Colour coding is very frequently used in displays, but is not necessarily superior to other means of conveying visual information, such as size or shape. Colours can be used effectively to group information displays and to highlight particular displays.

The eye is most sensitive to the colours blue–green–yellow, but this does vary as to whether the eye is adapted to light or dark conditions.

As the eye cannot focus all light wavelengths equivalently at one time, colours should not be superimposed on a display surface where those colours cannot be focussed simultaneously. For example, red characters should not be used on a blue background.

Colour does not affect the accuracy of reading as much as changes in

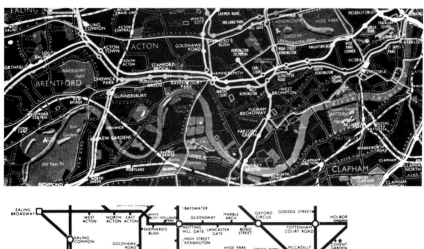

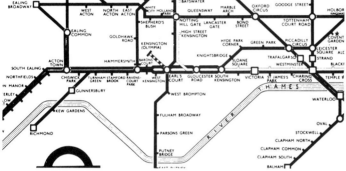

Figure 3.6 Two maps of the London Underground system: actual and representational. In the representational map, the central portion is larger in scale than outlying parts. For example, though the distance from Earl's Court to Richmond looks about the same as the distance from Earl's Court to Charing Cross, the former is 9.96 km (6.19 miles) and the latter is 6.08 km (3.78 miles).

brightness or contrast, suggesting that it is a superior coding device to these other methods.

No more than five colours should be used on a visual display, although under optimum viewing conditions as many as seven can be used.

It should always be remembered that some people are colour deficient, and so will be limited in the extent to which they can use the information contained in different colours. For example, red and green should not be used together, nor yellow and blue. In addition, some environments, such as radar rooms and, more commonly, streets, are lit by coloured lighting, and, because of this, surfaces whose colours are easily discriminated under white light may be indistinguishable under coloured light.

Developments in display technology

Research and development in the fields of electronic display technology, microprocessor technology, electronic transducer and monitor technology, and the applications of these devices and systems have made possible radical changes to the design of displays and the information they transmit. The visual display unit (VDU) is now fast becoming one of the most common display devices, and much effort has been devoted to the ergonomics problems associated with VDUs. Attention has been paid to the size and shape of characters displayed on a VDU, as well as their colour, contrast, density, and rate of presentation. Perhaps more importantly, a display driven by a microprocessor offers the designer not only a much wider range of characters and symbols than were possible with electromechanical displays, but also the option of a system with which the user can interact, selecting information as and when desired, in a variety of forms and at a number of levels of sophistication. In this sense, relatively greater emphasis has been placed on the nature of the information presented to the user (that is, factors relevant to understanding a display in addition to being able to read or hear it) than on its form alone.

Displays which incorporate computers, VDUs, light-emitting diodes, liquid crystals, and other devices must, clearly, meet the criteria of detectability, readability, and understandability described above. However, design recommendations for electromechanical displays may not be applicable to the design of these more recent devices, because of the technical differences in the ways that the images or sounds are generated. For instance, a light-emitting diode (LED), as the name suggests, is visible only because it creates its own light; a character created by an LED will therefore be brighter than its background—in contrast to most printed labels and characters, which are normally darker than their backgrounds. It has been shown that the difference between electromechanical and electronic display technologies leads to different ergonomics recommendations concerning character size, shape, and line thickness, and to base design specifications for LEDs on those for characters typically found in electromechanical displays would be wrong. Furthermore, specifications for LED displays may not be applicable to liquid crystal or vacuum fluorescent displays; hence the available data should be used carefully. There are other cases where, at present, no firm recommendations exist for display formats based on new technology: it is possible, for example, to present a combination of graphical (representational), textual (label), qualitative, and quantitative information together on one VDU screen in the form of a complex display. This was difficult or impossible with electromechanical devices. However, there are few firm recommendations about the format of such new displays (shape, size, position, etc) or about their content (meaningfulness). In such cases, the designer must resort to the experimental evaluation of displays which seem most likely to be satisfactory.

References at the end of the chapter contain further information about display design in general, and about each type in particular.

Relationships between displays, controls, and the world

Displays and controls are often associated; further, a display may have some direct relationship with an aspect of the outside world (Fig 3.7), as may a control. Indeed, the main display associated with a control may itself be a feature of the outside world (Fig 3.8). In general, people expect there to be certain relationships between both the position and direction of

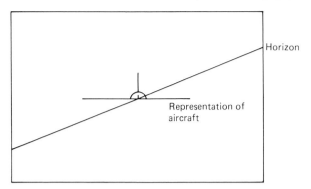

Figure 3.7 An aircraft attitude indicator shows the direct relationship between the wings of the aircraft and the horizon.

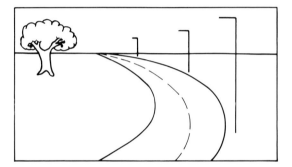

Figure 3.8 The main visual display for a car driver is the road ahead; the results of most control actions will change the nature of this display.

movement of related controls and displays, whether the displays are part of the outside world or 'within' the machine or system. These expectations are known as stereotypes. For instance, moving a horizontal slide control from left to right, or a rotary control clockwise, will normally be expected to move a corresponding display from left to right or clockwise, and these movements will normally be interpreted as an increase in the value of the controlled element (Fig 3.9). Stereotypes can be very powerful and, if ignored, can lead to errors. It is true that, with training and experience, a control–display relationship which does not conform to a stereotype can be learned. The danger comes when the control is used by a fatigued or stressed operator: in these cases, his or her behaviour may well revert to the stereotype. Many stereotypes are straightforward, and the ergonomics data will provide adequate guidance. In some cases, however, the stereotype may not be as clear, or may not exist at all. Confusion may occur if the control and display are in different planes, or if the value being controlled is unfamiliar to people: if a domestic air conditioning system had a humidity control operated by a rotary knob, would turning it clockwise mean more humidity (ie more water in the air) or more dryness? In such cases it may be necessary to carry out an experiment to resolve the issue.

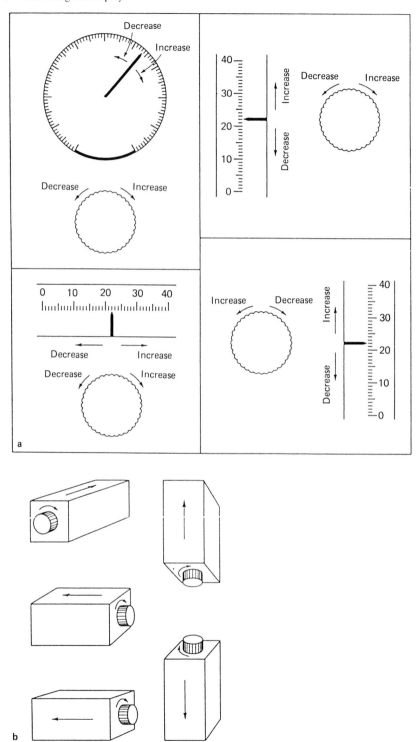

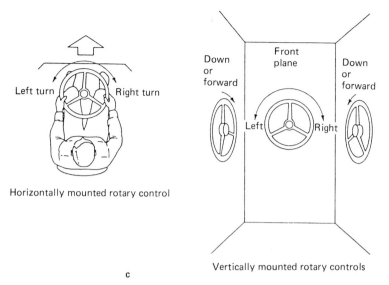

Left turn   Right turn

Horizontally mounted rotary control

Down or forward   Front plane   Down or forward

Left   Right

c

Vertically mounted rotary controls

Figure 3.9 Some examples of display–control stereotypes (after McCormick 1976): (a) illustration of desirable control–display movement relationships—fixed scales with moving pointer, with control in same plane as display; (b) illustration of some display–control relationships, showing the strongest relationships demonstrated by subjects; (c) the most compatible relationships between the direction of movement of horizontally and vertically mounted rotary controls and the response of vehicles.

Further reading

CAKIR, A., HART, D.J., and STEWART, T.F.M. (1980). *Visual display terminals*. New York: Wiley

DIFFRIENT, N., TILLEY, A.R., and HARMAN, D. (1981). *Humanscale 4/5/6*. Cambridge, Mass.: MIT Press

EASTEBY, R.S., and ZWAGA, H. (eds.) (1984). *Information Design*. New York: Wiley

GALER, M.D. and SIMMONDS, G.R.W. (1984). 'Ergonomic aspects of electronic instrumentation—a guide for designers'. Society of Automotive Engineers, paper SAE SP576

GALER, M.D. and SIMMONDS, G.R.W. (1985). 'The lighting of car instrument panels—drivers' responses to five colours'. Society of Automotive Engineers, paper SAE 850328

ERICCSON INFORMATION SYSTEMS, A.B. (1983). *Ergonomics principles in office automation*. Stockholm: EIS AB

McCORMICK, E.J. (1976). *Human Factors in Engineering and Design*. New York: McGraw-Hill

McCORMICK, E.J. and SANDERS, M.S. (1982). *Human Factors in Engineering and Design*, 5th edn. New York: McGraw-Hill.

NATIONAL ELECTRONICS COUNCIL (1983). *Human Factors and Information Technology*. London: NEC

SCHUBERT, E. (1975). Comparative studies of the readability of CRT generated displays. Society for Information Displays, Symposium digest of technical papers, pp. 96–97

SINGLETON, W.T. (1969). *Ergonomics* **12**.4. 519–531. Display design: principles and procedures

VAN COTT, H.P. and KINKADE, R.G. (eds) (1972). *Human engineering guide to equipment design*. Washington, DC: US Government Printing Office

WOODSON, W.E. (1981). *Human factors design handbook*. New York: McGraw-Hill

Chapter 4

The design of controls

In this chapter we deal with the main features of the design of hand and foot controls. Criteria for controls are given, and we consider the relationship between controls, their uses, and their functions. Special control devices are also discussed.

Controls were developed as extensions of the human body. This extension was made to allow the generation of more power, more reach, and a reduction in effort and risk to the user. Simple tools characterise these extensions very well: in the hands of an experienced user they become literal extensions of the arms and legs, and facilitate the performance of tasks that would otherwise be impossible. For example, a spanner can tighten a nut far more tightly than is possible by the bare hand; a knife or chisel concentrates the force applied in a very small area, creating a cutting action; a scythe enables a large area of grass to be cut in one sweep; a pair of kitchen tongs reduces the chances of the user being burned by contact with hot surfaces and materials.

From these simple tools, larger machines were developed further to extend human ability and to relieve people of the need to expend large amounts of energy. However, whilst cranes, mechanical diggers, and fork lift trucks relieve the user of much heavy physical work and the need to use manual tools, they have presented problems of a different sort. The same can be said of machines which relieve the user of information-processing work, such as computers. The human ability to control the human body must be transferred to control of the movement and operation of the machine and its components. The control is no longer the tool itself, but is an intermediary between the user and the machine. Actions taken by the user may be separated in space and time from the result of those actions. As a result, the control must do more than merely fit the body of the user: it must be able to indicate its function independently of the machine component it affects, it must indicate its method of operation, and it may have to indicate the result of some operation. In other words, it may become one of the few parts of the machine visible to the user, replacing a direct line of communication between the two, and as such must do far more than the traditional tool could. Because of this, controls must be designed to meet human capabilities and limitations if the whole unit—user and machine—is to work at maximum efficiency.

50

Criteria for control design

Just as a display must be detectable, readable, and understandable, so, analogously, a control must be accessible, identifiable, and usable.

Accessibility. If they are large enough or loud enough, displays can be located at any distance from the operator. Since virtually all controls require physical contact with the user, they must be able to be reached comfortably and efficiently; the body size of the user must be considered. A control that cannot be reached, or can be reached only with difficulty, is useless.

Identifiability. In many cases the control needs explicit identification, either because it is one of a number of controls located close together or because it must be identified without visual guidance. The problem of identification may be divided into two parts: identifying the basic function of the control (eg power switch, turn indicator, typewriter shift key) and identifying the state of the control or the system component to which it relates (eg on/off, low/medium/high, up/down). Both these problems, however, may be solved by coding the control in some way. Coding may be effected by designing controls to have different shapes (Fig 4.1), textures, sizes, colours, positions, labels, or operational methods (for example, a control that moves only from left to right will be distinguished from one that moves up and down). The efficiency of coding can be enhanced if more than one coding method is used at the same time; this is particularly useful if the control is used in both daytime and night-time conditions, when coding by, say, colour may be complemented by shape coding.

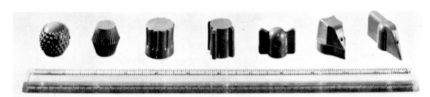

Figure 4.1 This range of shaped control knobs is the result of research into recognition by touch. Experiments with large numbers of blindfolded subjects have shown that the knobs are never confused.

Usability. If the user can reach the control, knows what it is and what state it is in, then the next step is to change its state—it must be used. Two human factors are involved here: one relates to the force required to operate the control, and the other to the ability of the user to make fine adjustments. The first issue is one of muscle power, and the relation between power, the position of the limb when the power is applied, and the length of time the power is applied. The second issue contains an element of muscle power, but is largely a psychological, not a physical, problem. A system for which a very small movement of the control leads to a very large movement of the element being controlled may be difficult to use because the user may not be able to make such small movements reliably. The tuning knobs on some radio receivers suffer from this fault, with the result that it is difficult to tune to a station without a lot of concentration and effort. On the other hand, a control for which a large movement means a small change in the controlled element may require a lot of time for its operation, although it would be very accurate. This problem is known as 'control gearing', and a number of recommendations have been made for the optimum gearing of several types of control.

Once the control action has been made, the user needs some acknowledgement of the action. For some controls, this 'feedback' may take the form of an audible 'click' by the control, or at least a moving control coming to a definite stop. In other cases, the system being controlled will assume an obvious, and different, state—such as a moving car coming to a halt. In yet others, the state of the control will again be identified by means of coding. Finally the control may be associated with a display which shows the new system value.

Controls and their users

Just as the energy output of the human body is limited, so the movements which people can make are restricted by the range within which parts of the body can move. The height of the user may determine the location of a control; the weight of the user might be important if large forces have to be exerted on a handle or lever; the anatomical structure of the hand will determine the relative functions of the fingers and thumb in the design of a keyboard (Fig 4.2).

Control location and the user. The positioning of a control will depend heavily on its function, but it also depends on the sex and age of the users,

Figure 4.2 This text-entering device is designed to be used with one hand. The keys are laid out to fit the shape of the hand and the positions of the fingers.

because of differences in the sizes of men and women and of differences in strength between young and old people. There are also differences in body size and strength between people in different countries (the 50th percentile male stature is 1748 mm in the USA: in Japan it is 1669 mm), as well as differences in convention concerning the way that controls are used. Machines intended for use in different countries must be designed with this variation in mind: if tractors designed to accommodate British farmers were sent to certain parts of the world, the majority of people would not even be able to reach the pedals! These major differences aside, there are further differences which may affect control location. For example, whilst most people are right-handed, placing all controls to the right of the user will handicap left-handed people. Thus where a control is particularly important or requires continuous operation, it is best located where it can be used easily by either hand or by both at once. There is a wide range of published data on body size and strength, and some of the main sources are given at the end of this chapter.

Muscles and movement. Limbs are moved by muscles acting about joints; the range, speed, accuracy, and force of a particular movement depends on the part of the body involved. Some parts are better suited to particular purposes than others: the legs, for example, can exert very large forces in certain directions; the shoulder has the greatest range of movement of any joint in the body; and the hands and fingers are capable of the finest and most delicate manipulations.

Posture and fatigue. Absence of actual movement in the body does not mean absence of physical work: some parts of the body are always working, even during sleep. Much of this activity is aimed at the maintenance of

Figure 4.3 Three increasingly effective control positions for writing: (a) the whole weight of the arm is on the shoulder; (b) a local support (the edge of the hand) provides greater control and accuracy; (c) the support is extended along the forearm to the elbow, allowing continuous control whilst the hand moves across the paper.

posture in the spine and head, and in maintaining the desired position of the limbs. Fatigue can result from an excessive demand to maintain posture or position, but it can often be minimised by the provision of suitable supports in the form of seats and rests for the limbs. It is sometimes essential to provide local support to stabilise the hands or feet if fine control adjustments must be made, particularly in conditions of vibration and jolting. For instance, most people write with the forearm supported on a table or other surface; it is much more difficult to perform this delicate task with the forearm unsupported, because energy is needed to maintain the position, and because the whole arm becomes involved in the writing task, rather than the hand and wrist alone (Fig 4.3). Local support can sometimes be designed into the control itself: the use of a knob rather than a lever allows the user's hand to be steadied by grasping the control, and the turning movement is less affected by motion or jolting. A user can also be steadied by using both arms in opposition to one another, as in using the steering wheel of a car.

Controls and their functions

The function of a control will determine its location, identification and design, irrespective of whether the control is to be used on a tractor, a computer, or an aircraft. The range of possible functions is discussed below in terms of the force, speed, and accuracy of control movements.

Force

A control should require the application of a large force only if it falls into one of the following categories:

• those used in an emergency, as for example in the event of a power failure;
• those which are used only occasionally and where power operation is considered unnecessary;
• those which are operated by hand-tools during maintenance work.

The amount of force a user can exert on a control depends on posture, position, and the length of time the force is applied. When it is applied to a hand or foot control, the rest of the body must provide a stable base from which to work and to resist movement. In some cases, the body can be kept steady by grasping some adjacent fixture, although body weight itself can often be adequate to counteract the reaction to the exerted force.

There is much published information on the forces people can exert in various limb movements, although this should be used with care: many studies have been concerned with maximum strength over a short period (eg 5 seconds) with little or no displacement of the limb. 'Jerk' forces used to loosen tight controls may be two or three times larger than the corresponding maximum steady forces; forces which must be applied over a long period should, it has been suggested, not exceed 15% of the corresponding maximum force over 5 seconds, although such continuous application may last for an hour or more without rest. On the other hand, a large force may reasonably be required if it is intermittently applied over a long period (eg a day).

As mentioned above, there is much variation between people in the amount of force that can be applied. Accordingly, an emergency control should need less force to operate than the weakest person can exert, although it should not be so light as to be operated by an accidental knock. Human strength is also affected by temperature: a manual control that can be used in warm weather may be more difficult to use in the cold (Fig 4.4).

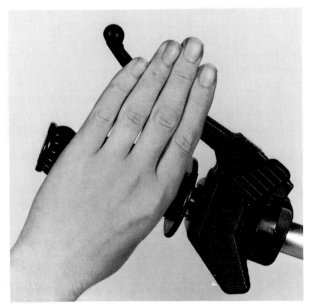

Figure 4.4 A hand operating a motorcycle brake lever in many cases is exposed to low temperatures caused by the ambient temperature and the chilling effect of the wind. This cooling can reduce the ability of the hand to exert force on the lever.

One of the most important factors affecting the steady force which can be applied to a control is its position relative to the body and to the muscles and joints used. For example, so long as there is adequate support for the body, the maximum torque that a seated operator can exert on a hand-wheel with both hands can be achieved by placing the control so that the shoulder muscles are employed, rather than those which bend or straighten the elbow. Similarly, the force which a seated operator can apply to a foot pedal depends on a good backrest and the degree to which the knees are bent (Fig 4.5). It has been found that the knee angle at which the maximum force can be applied is about the same for everyone, and that this angle is critical.

Another important principle concerns the relationship between maximum force and endurance. Research has shown that the limb position in which the operator can apply the maximum force on a control is also the most favourable one for applying a smaller force for the greatest length of

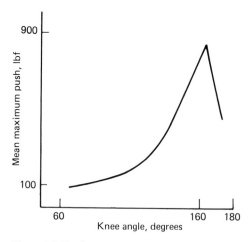

Figure 4.5 The force exerted on a foot pedal by a seated person, as a function of knee angle. Note that the exertable force increases sharply as the knee angle increases, to a maximum when the angle is about 160°. Thereafter it decreases rapidly. (After Hugh-Jones 1947)

time. Thus if a control is placed so that the maximum force can be applied to it, then the chances of the operator becoming fatigued are minimised.

Speed and range

The speed of a control movement depends on many features of the task, such as the accuracy and force required, the range or amplitude of the movement, the type of control, and so forth. A hand-crank is the most suitable control for quick, continuous manual adjustments over a wide range of control movements, whilst handwheels and knobs are recommended where the range of movement is relatively small. The speed with which a rotary control such as a crank or knob can be turned is governed largely by the resistance to be overcome, as well as by the diameter of the control, the plane of operation (horizontal or vertical), and the direction of rotation (clockwise or anticlockwise). Training is likely to have an effect on this type of task, and the operator will perform better if the preferred hand is used.

Most hand controls can be operated more speedily if they are located at, or just below, elbow height (Fig 4.6), which is also the best position for continuous or frequent use. This is true whether the operator sits or stands.

The limb movement which produces the maximum speed is not always the one which can apply the maximum force or the greatest accuracy; it is always necessary to decide which is the most important criterion for a particular problem. In a complex skill such as keyboard use, which involves fast and sequential operation of the fingers, the links between the movements (or keys) may be more important than the relative tapping speeds of the fingers themselves. Only a careful analysis of the task can indicate the critical features of the control operation required.

In general, the greater the range of movement required, the longer it will

a   b

 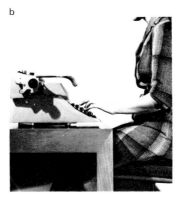

Figure 4.6 In typing, as in many other hand-controlled operations, more speed is obtained if the controls are located at, or just below, elbow height (b), rather than the more common position (a). Position (b) is also less likely to lead to strain in the hands, arms and shoulders

take to complete. However, for relatively small ranges of movement, most of the time taken to make a control response is spent in starting and stopping the movement. The start is likely to be delayed if the response involves a decision of some sort: for example, if a choice must be made between alternative actions. A simple response to an expected signal can be initiated in about 0.2 seconds, but if the operator does not know which of several possible signals may be presented, and yet each signal has its own appropriate response, the time lag may be appreciably longer. Also, if the operator cannot predict when a signal will occur, it will take appreciably longer to initiate the response. But if the operator knows in advance the responses to be made (as in typing the sequence of letters in a word) the movements can be 'programmed' and the time interval between them can be minimised. Similarly, the time taken to stop a control movement depends on the level of accuracy required and the degree to which the end point can be anticipated.

Accuracy

The accuracy of a control movement depends on the nature of the operator and the design of the control, and, very importantly, on the clear presentation of information about the effect of the control action (feedback). Accuracy implies matching the controlled object to some sort of target, as in directing a crane to a pickup point, or the cursor on a computer screen to a desired position; or matching it to a path, as in guiding an aircraft on a desired compass heading. Irrespective of experience, few people would attempt these sorts of tasks without visual or other forms of guidance. Adequate information must be given concerning the location of both the target and the controlled object if they are to be matched. These tasks all concern the problem of 'tracking' and have received much attention from both psychologists and engineers, particularly in relation to military and aviation problems.

In such situations, the operator must first bring the control into line with the target and then make continuous adjustments to maintain the desired position or direction. If direction must be maintained, and the desired course ahead cannot be seen, information is needed about the past and present state of the target to help predict its future behaviour. Full and immediate information is also needed on the results of control actions, so that the error or discrepancy is known between the target and follower in order to minimise this quickly.

The operator must be thoroughly familiar with the characteristics of the controls before an appropriate response can be made to a given difference between target and follower. Unfortunately, the desirable control characteristics for the fast and accurate location of a target are likely to be different from those most suitable for continuous, small adjustment actions: the control sensitivity (called gearing) needs to be relatively coarse for the initial, approximate movement of the follower onto the target, but fine for the subsequent, accurate secondary adjustments. A compromise is often needed to satisfy both of these requirements simultaneously (Fig 4.7).

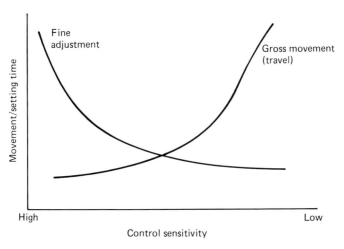

Figure 4.7 Sensitivity and movement time for a hand-operated control. If sensitivity is high (small control movement produces large display movement) it will be relatively difficult and time consuming to make a fine adjustment, but relatively easy to make large (travel) changes to the display. The position is reversed for low-sensitivity controls.

Other factors

Some aspects of control performance, such as the 'feel' of the controls, are difficult to define but nevertheless are very important. An experienced driver, for instance, knows when the car is on a greasy or icy road surface by the lighter steering quality as well as by the reduced effectiveness of the steering wheel; small differences in the mechanical design of keys on a keyboard can give the keyboard a quite different feel, with consequent effects on the performance and satisfaction of the user.

One factor affecting the feel of controls is the type of resistance they offer. This resistance can be created simply by the use of spring loading (which brings the control back to its initial or neutral position after use); by designing static friction into the control, such that initial movement is made more difficult; by viscous resistance, where the resisting force is proportional to the speed with which the control is moved; and by inertial resistance, where the resisting force is proportional to the acceleration of the control. Each of these types of resistance has advantages and drawbacks for particular applications, and resistance, with the 'feel' it generates, acts as an important source of feedback to the user: a spring-loaded control will offer increasing resistance as the control is moved further from its starting position, and the user can make use of this information in judging where the control is at a particular time.

It is sometimes desirable to design resistance into controls which would otherwise offer little or no resistance because the control mechanism is power assisted. It is true that power assistance can relieve the user of the need to expend much muscular energy, although, if too much assistance is given, an important source of feedback is lost, and the control may be activated accidentally. The nature of power operation is also important: it may be such as to move the controlled element a distance proportional to that moved by the control (called position control), in the way that the tuning control on a radio moves the pointer from one station to another. However, some controls operate such that a change in the position of the control results in a proportional rate of change in the controlled element (called velocity controls). The steering wheel of a car may be described as a velocity control in that the rate of change of direction of the car depends on the position of the wheel. It is even possible to make controls for which a change in position of the control leads to a change in acceleration in the controlled element, rather than in velocity or position. There are some recommendations concerning such exotic devices, but frequently it is necessary to evaluate alternative solutions to a specific problem experimentally.

Choosing the best control

The various types of control—switches, levers, pedals, sliders, touch-sensitive panels, keys, and a myriad of others—enable the user to select information and to govern a process. When designing a control, or evaluating an existing installation, clear answers must be obtained to the following questions.

What is the control meant to do, and how important is this function to the operation of the whole system? This will indicate the priorities by which the control should be designed; one that is central to the operation of the whole system (for example, the keyboard on a computer) and a deficiency in which would have major consequences, merits closer attention than one whose purpose is peripheral to the system (for example, the bonnet release catch on a car). In an ideal world, both of these examples would receive the same attention and concern, but this may not be possible in practice.

Should the control be designed primarily to allow rapid operation, accurate operation, or the application of a relatively large force? This will suggest not only the body component which should operate the control, but also the broad design features of the control itself. Large forces, for example, are more readily applied by the legs and feet than the arms and hands; as suggested above, rapid operation may be facilitated by a control with high gearing (low sensitivity), whilst accurate operation may demand low gearing: a control knob for accurate use may need to be larger than one for which the accuracy requirement is less stringent.

For whom is the control to be designed, and under what conditions will it be used? Populations differ in their ability to exert force, make accurate movements, and make fast movements. For example, elderly people are more likely than the young to suffer some form of arthritis in the joints, and as a result their manipulative ability is limited; children are generally less able to make accurate movements than adults because their visual–motor co-ordination is not fully developed. Because of these differences, a control designed for one group may not be as easy to use by members of another group. Thus the control designer or selector must, as a fundamental consideration, take the capacities of the user population into account: controls for a general, open market should be designed to be usable by all members of the general population, whereas those intended for specialised equipment, such as aircraft controls or medical equipment, would not need to be so accommodating.

Questions about the population can be extended to wider aspects of ability. It is known, for example, that the acquisition of typing skill, for use on a typewriter or computer keyboard, takes much time and practice; most people do not have this skill, and cannot be expected to acquire it. A computer-based system employing a conventional keyboard would therefore present difficulties to many people, and unless the user is prepared to learn to type quickly, or unless the characters to be entered are few and the task is to be done only occasionally, or unless there is no time penalty attached to the task, then some alternative to the keyboard might be desirable. This may take a number of forms, such as keys which select a whole function rather than entering a single character, devices such as graphics tablets which avoid the need for a keyboard, and systems which recognise speech rather than requiring the input of information by some manual action.

As well as the user, the environment should be taken into account. Some controls will need to be used in darkness, in extremes of climate, and even in conditions of reduced or zero gravity. All these, and other environmental conditions, will affect the design of the control: ones used in darkness, for example, will need to be identifiable by touch, whilst those used in very hot climates may need to have a textured surface to reduce the chances of the control slipping in a sweaty hand; a control to be used in very cold conditions will need to be designed for use by a gloved hand.

What are the task requirements for the control, beyond general questions of force, speed, and accuracy? Considerations under this heading will determine many of the detailed design features of the control. In some applications, for example, the operator will need to select one of a small range of settings or positions, rather than a continuously variable value. In this case, a control should be provided that has definite switched positions, or even a number of push-buttons or keys, each of which selects a particular value; this is found in many car radios, in addition to a tuning knob which provides the opportunity to select infrequently-used stations. Most domestic televisions use push-buttons for channel selection, whereas older models often employed a continuous tuning control.

What other tasks will be carried out by the operator, and with what controls? Few jobs are carried out with the use of only one control. Frequently, a variety of controls and displays are used and are located in the same workspace. This fact has implications for the design of individual controls: since it is desirable for a set of tasks to be distributed evenly between the four limbs, the designer may have no option but to assign a task to the hand, say, when it would preferably be assigned to the foot and leg. In other cases, the design of one control may need to be made similar to that of another if the need is for consistency of design; or it may need to be made different if it is important that two controls should be easily distinguished.

Controls and advanced technology

Developments in computer and information technology have made available to the designer a range of control devices that previously were to be found only in science fiction. These include typewriter-like keyboards, special keyboards employing a relatively small number of keys, each controlling complete functions rather than individual characters, touch-sensitive panels and keys, light pens, hand-held cursors, and similar devices. At the time of writing of this book, rapid progress is being made on the design of machines which can recognise human speech as a control medium—a function that could previously be employed only when communicating with other humans and not with machines. Even the expression 'the push-button age' is fast becoming outdated as push-button keyboards are being complemented by other control types.

One aspect of this development is that, in the computer applications field at least, the device being controlled is information, and not a physical entity with a mass that has to be moved. In other cases, the work of manipulating a mass is performed by servo systems, and not by some mechanical gearing system which must be designed to accommodate the limitations of human strength. A railway routing system is now controlled by means of servo-operated points controlled by keys and buttons, and not by mechanical levers in the signal box; the power units and generators in large ships also are controlled from a keyboard, rather than the operator having to struggle with heavy wheel-operated valves and with control levers. The result of both these developments is that the problems of designing controls have been in one sense simplified, by removing the need to exert large forces and to adopt, or accommodate, certain operator postures. However, the emphasis has changed, so that control design must take into account the ability of the operator to acquire psychologically-determined manual skills, such as keyboard usage, which require little physical effort but whose satisfactory completion is limited by psychological factors.

The well-established ergonomics literature will provide the designer with usable information concerning the design of keyboards and other devices by which people can communicate with computer-based systems. In addition, there are at the time of writing a number of texts aimed directly at problems such as keyboard design. References to these are given at the end of this chapter. However, much basic and applied work has yet to be carried out to investigate the ergonomics features of new control devices, and whilst reports of such work are to be found in scientific journals, there are many instances where ergonomics knowledge is deficient. In these cases, the designer has little option but to achieve the best solution possible on the basis of incomplete design information, and then to evaluate that solution by means of experimentation.

Special control devices

Most people are fortunate enough to have full use of their arms and legs, and most controls are designed for use by these limbs. In some cases, however, disease or injury means that the arms or legs cannot be used, and it is necessary to design control devices that can be used by people disabled in this way.

Figure 4.8 In this car, tasks normally carried out by the legs and feet via pedals have been reassigned to the hands and arms, allowing control of the car by people with physical impairment of the legs.

In some cases, the design problem is fairly straightforward, in that a task normally carried out by the foot and leg is assigned to the hand and arm. For example, motor cars can be modified so that the clutch, brake, and throttle are controlled by the hand rather than the feet (Fig 4.8). The only reservation here is that the hands and arms do not become overloaded by the additional tasks, both in terms of the forces that have to be applied, and of the number of tasks to be done. Beyond this, however, devices have been produced which allow those with severe physical impairment to control the world around them and to communicate with it. These involve capitalising on very limited types and ranges of movement—sometimes solely the ability to raise a finger or to exhale air—and using these to operate switches and keys. It is, of course, impossible to achieve a level of performance with these devices equivalent to that which can be achieved by conventional controls in the hands of able-bodied people, but they provide a vital link with the world for the handicapped individual.

Example: choosing a control

Controls vary widely in design, ranging from simple on–off push-buttons and toggle switches to more complex two-dimensional joysticks. Based on experimental evidence it is possible to make recommendations for the most appropriate control and its desirable range of operation in a particular situation.

Table 4.1 Suitability of various controls for different purposes

Type of Control	Suitability for tasks involving:			
	Speed	Accuracy	Force	Range
Cranks				
Small	Good	Poor	Unsuitable	Good
Large	Poor	Unsuitable	Good	Good
Handwheels	Poor	Good	Fair/Poor	Fair
Knobs	Unsuitable	Fair	Unsuitable	Fair
Levers				
Horizontal	Good	Poor	Poor	Poor
Vertical				
(to–from body)	Good	Fair	Short: Poor Long: Good	Poor
(across body)	Fair	Fair	Fair	Unsuitable
Joysticks	Good	Fair	Poor	Poor
Pedals	Good	Poor	Good	Unsuitable
Push-buttons	Good	Unsuitable	Unsuitable	Unsuitable
Rotary selector switch	Good	Good	Unsuitable	Unsuitable
Joystick selector switch	Good	Good	Poor	Unsuitable

A brief summary of the availability of different types of control for different purposes is given in Table 4.1.

Further reading

BAILEY, R.W. (1982). *Human performance engineering; a guide for system designers*. London: Prentice-Hall

CAKIR, A., HART, D.J., and STEWART, T.F.M. (1980). *Visual display terminals*. New York: Wiley

DIFFRIENT, N., TILLEY, A.R., AND HARMAN, D. (1981). *Humanscale 4/5/6*. Cambridge, Mass.: MIT Press

ERICSSON INFORMATION SYSTEMS AB (1983). *Ergonomics principles in office automation*. Stockholm: EIS AB

HUGH-JONES, P. (1947). *J. Physiol*, **105**, 332–344. 'The effect of limb position in seated subjects on their ability to utilize the maximum contractile force of the limb muscles.'

MCCORMICK, E.J. and SANDERS, M. (1983). *Human factors in engineering and design*. New York: McGraw-Hill

PHEASANT, S.T. (1984). *Anthropometrics: an introduction for schools and colleges*. London: BSI

VAN COTT, H.P. and KINKADE, R.G. (1972). *Human engineering guide to equipment design*. Washington, DC: US Government Printing Office

WOODSON, W. (1981). *Human factors design handbook*. New York: Wiley

Chapter 5

Layout of panels and machines

Important features in the positioning of controls and displays are introduced in this chapter. These include the relationships between associated controls and displays, sequential operation, functional grouping, and emergency considerations.

We have seen that the design of individual displays and controls can affect the efficiency with which they are used by an operator. The relationship between the movement of a control and that of an associated display has also been discussed. Beyond these principles, however, it is necessary to consider the design of arrays of controls and displays: these are frequently found in industrial machines controlling a number of parameters, in the fascia panels of cars and trucks, in computer workstations, and a variety of other applications.

Designing an array of controls and displays can present problems, especially if a number of different tasks have to be performed with them. For example, a computer may be used for word processing, calculation, database management, list keeping, and machine language programming, and the best layout of alphanumeric keys, special function keys, cursor controls, and the like may differ for each of these tasks. A compromise must be reached which most nearly satisfies all of these requirements, and the designer must take care to minimise the conflicts that may arise.

Some general principles

One or more of four criteria should be satisfied when designing an array of controls and displays, as follows.

Sequence of use. Some tasks always follow a fixed sequence of operations. For example, the order in which the functions and systems of an aircraft are checked prior to a flight may be fixed. In the home, some microwave cookers require that specifications of food type, weight, cooking intensity, and cooking time be carried out in a fixed sequence. Where this sort of sequence is important, the controls and displays should be set out in an order that reflects the sequence. This makes the task easier to perform, because the user does not have to remember the order but instead operates from left to right or from top to bottom of an array of controls and displays. The time taken to perform the task will be reduced because thinking time and movement time between different controls and displays is minimised. Fewer errors also will be made.

Frequency of use. Different controls and displays may not be used in a set sequence but, even so, some may be used more often than others. In general, the most frequently used controls and displays will be placed nearest to the operator, again minimising search time for the right display and control, and reducing errors. In a motor car, the speedometer is normally placed directly in front of the driver because it is one of the most frequently read displays.

Importance of use. The driver of a racing car is certainly concerned with how fast the car is travelling, but is more concerned with the speed of the engine, expressed in revolutions per minute. This information indicates when gear changes should be made for optimum power output, and whether the engine is running dangerously fast. For this reason, the 'rev counter' is placed directly in front of the driver in the most prominent position. In general, warning indicators, and controls which control the primary, and most important, functions of a system, are placed near to the operator. Many controls and displays which are frequently used are often the most important as well, and so the 'frequency' and 'importance' principles may lead to the same solution; however, there are cases, as in emergency indicators, where the most important functions are the least likely to occur.

Function. Frequently, groups of controls and displays within a larger set are associated with particular functions. A computer keyboard, for instance, may have a cluster of alphabetic keys arranged in the familiar QWERTY layout, and a separate cluster of numeric keys. The former might be used for text entry, and the latter for data entry. Cursor control keys also may be grouped (Fig 5.1). A more specialised example of this is

Figure 5.1 The keys on the keyboard of this microcomputer are grouped according to their function. There are clusters of alphabetic, numeric, special function, and cursor control keys.

Figure 5.2 A specialised keyboard for use in a hospital ward to collect patient data. The keys are arranged in groups according to which aspect of the patient they refer.

shown in Fig. 5.2. This is the design for a keyboard for the entry of data about patients in a hospital ward. The parameters to be entered are arranged in groups on the keyboard, corresponding to function: there is a group all relating to consciousness level, another for respiration, one for monitoring tests, and so on. Arranging the keys in this way reflects the way in which the patient is observed, and in addition prompts the clinician to enter all the relevant information for a given group.

Clearly, it will not always be possible to satisfy the four criteria of sequence, frequency, importance, and function simultaneously. Indeed, they might give conflicting results. However, it is possible that, within subgroups of control and display elements defined by one principle, the elements can be arranged within that group according to another principle. For example, a large number of controls and displays may be arranged into subgroups in terms of function, and the individual elements within those groups arranged according to sequence of use. In other cases, it may be that one criterion is more important than the others, and will largely determine the final layout. As always, the tasks to be carried out with the controls and displays must be clearly understood, as must the consequences of error or slow performance.

In general, however, the analyst will carry out a design by grouping in the following way: first, four lists are prepared of the controls and displays separately:

(1) items considered most important for the task involved;
(2) the items used most frequently in regular operation;
(3) any items used together in a sub-sequence;
(4) any items related to each other by function.

The lists are not mutually exclusive, and several items may appear in more than one category.

In designing the layout, those items on the important and frequently used lists are placed near the centre of the panel or console, in easily accessible and well-differentiated positions. The items in sub-sequences are placed together, perhaps in a row or column, and the functionally

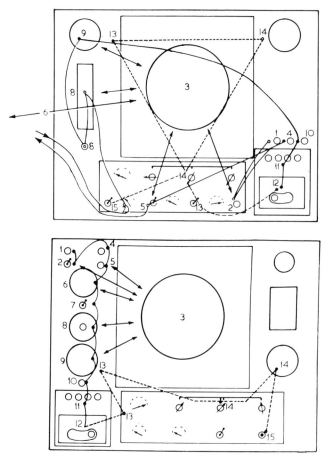

Figure 5.3 Link analysis applied to the redesign of a panel layout: (a) sequence of operations required by a prototype panel layout; (b) redesigned layout after analysis of operating sequence.

related items are similarly placed in groups together, with some visual and spatial separation from other items.

Figure 5.3 gives an example of design by sequence. It involves an assessment technique which can be applied to the design of workplace and room layouts as well as to that of panels, and which is called link analysis. Link analysis requires that the operation of the controls and displays on the panel be observed or anticipated. This yields data about the order in which tasks are carried out, and the order in which displays are consulted and controls used. In some cases, the frequency of eye or limb movements from one component to another is recorded, as is the distance of such movements. In a larger problem, such as the layout of a workroom containing a number of machines which together form a process, the frequency and distances of movements of people and materials from one machine to another may be recorded, as well as the points in the room where paths cross. In general, the purpose of a link analysis is to point to those areas where sequences of movements or actions are too complex, where excessive distances have to be travelled, particularly with a high frequency, and where conflicts of movements occur. Fig 5.3 shows a version of a panel of controls and displays, on which have been drawn lines representing the sequence of eye or hand movements necessary to operate the equipment. It is clear from Fig 5.3 that this sequence is very jumbled. The figure also shows the corresponding sequence after the panel has been redesigned: this shows a much more ordered series of movements, and it would be expected that the equipment would be easier to operate with this version than with the first.

General suggestions

If a panel contains a large number of visual displays, the user may have difficulty picking out the right one. In addition to ensuring that the displays are in good contrast to their background, perhaps by means of colour coding, a distinct patterning of the displays may help, as illustrated in Fig 5.4. Patterning can also assist check reading, for if the displays are of the same format, and are oriented so that each normal reading appears in the

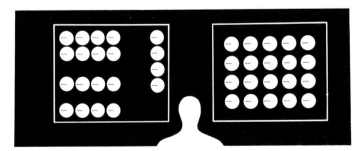

Figure 5.4 Logical groupings within a bank of dials enable the operator to easily identify a particular dial.

same position on the display, any deviant value will stand out clearly. Experiments have shown that such a panel can be checked more quickly than a haphazard arrangement: indeed, as much as an 800% improvement has been observed. However, the practical application of this principle raises certain problems, such as allowing for drift, and providing suitable rotatable displays to align the pointers; general purpose solutions are difficult to define.

The idea of grouping and patterning can also be applied to the design of panels of controls. A row of identical keys or switches, for example, may be aesthetically pleasing, but profoundly confusing to the user. If a number of controls on a panel have to be the same shape or size, then grouping or colour coding can provide a useful indication of function. Those controls which have to be used without visual guidance may be discriminated if they have easily distinguishable shapes, as noted in the last chapter.

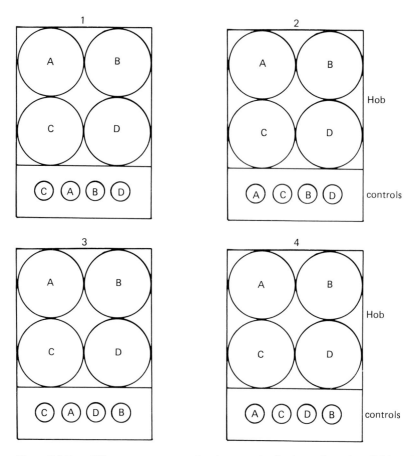

Figure 5.5 Four different arrangements for the controls of a domestic cooker. Subjects in an experiment made less than half the number of errors of operation with layout 4 than with layouts 2 or 3. Layout 4 was also preferred by more people than any of the other layouts. (After Ray and Ray 1979)

Associated controls and displays should be placed near each other, with the control near the display or to its right, so that the user's hand does not interfere with reading. If related controls and displays must be on separate panels, they should be arranged in the same order, so that it is easy to relate a control to its display. This problem arises in the design of cooker controls: here, the display is the radiant or gas ring, and the controls are normally located together by the side of the set of rings, or below them. Fig 5.5 shows the best arrangement for controls located below the cooker hob, and experiments have shown that this arrangement leads to significantly fewer errors than other arrangements.

Most controls can be operated equally well by either hand. The preferred hand is better, however, for fine, accurate adjustment, and such controls should be placed in a central position to accommodate both right- and left-handed people.

Labels should be placed above controls, so that they are always visible, and, since consistency in layout helps the user, labels should also be placed above their respective displays.

Planning for emergency becomes increasingly more important as machines become more complex. Whilst sophisticated automatic failure detectors may be incorporated in some advanced machines and systems, in many cases rapid human action is still required in the event of an emergency. The effectiveness of this action often depends on the arrangement of controls and displays. First, the user must be alerted quickly and should then be able to locate the fault with the minimum delay. To do this, auditory alarms are often desirable, supplemented by a visual display which gives further information about the problem. Second, it is well known that people under stress often revert to simple, well-learned habits (stereotypes). This means that the expected relationships between control and display directions of movement, illustrated in Fig 3.9, become even more important in cases of emergency.

Examples of control and display layout

Many people are familiar with the conventional layout of a typewriter keyboard, known as the QWERTY layout (Fig 5.6). This was first developed in the late nineteenth century, and its purpose was to ensure that the key bars of letters which frequently occur in pairs were not next to each other. This reduced the chance of the bars fouling each other when the two letters were keyed rapidly and successively. The layout was not designed to maximise the speed with which material can be typed, nor to minimise the number of user errors, nor to fulfil any other direct ergonomics criterion. Since the establishment of the QWERTY layout, alternatives have been suggested which are claimed more closely to meet ergonomics criteria, and a number of experimental investigations have been made to evaluate these. These alternatives are technically feasible, because modern typewriters and computer keyboards do not use key bars to carry the letter forms; instead, a 'golf ball' may be used, or a 'daisy wheel', or the characters may be created electronically on a CRT screen. Perhaps the best known of the

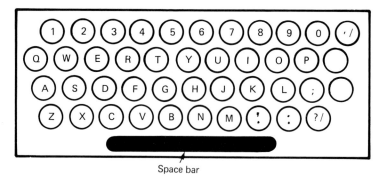

Space bar

Figure 5.6 Conventional, QWERTY keyboard layout.

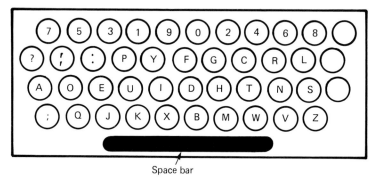

Space bar

Figure 5.7 Dvorak keyboard layout.

alternative layouts is the Dvorak design (Fig 5.7). The most radical alternative is the PCD-Maltron design (Fig 5.8); according to the manufacturers, this lays the keys out such that 90% of the letters of the 100 most used English words are on the 'home' row under the resting position of the fingers. In addition, the keys are arranged to accommodate the unequal length of the fingers, and to make more extensive use of the thumbs. The makers also claim that the layout makes it more difficult for the fingers to stray to the wrong keys. In all, a 20%-40% increase in typing speed is claimed, with no confusion for those who switch to the new layout having been trained using the QWERTY layout.

A different approach to the problem of keyboard design is represented by the employment of chord keying—that is, pressing more than one key at a time—as an alternative to the conventional keyboard with one key per character. At the time of writing, a device called a 'Microwriter' is available which employs only six keys, combinations of which represent all the characters found on a conventional keyboard. The device is used by one hand only and it is claimed that the skill necessary for rapid use of the device can be acquired within a few days (Fig 4.2 shows a Microwriter).

Figure 5.8 PCD-Maltron keyboard layout.

Further reading

McCORMICK, E.J. and SANDERS, M.S. (1982). *Human Factors in engineering and design*, 5th edn. New York: McGraw-Hill.

RAY, R.D. and RAY, W.D. (1979). 'An analysis of domestic cooker control design', *Ergonomics*, **22**, 11, 1243

VAN COTT, H.P. and KINKADE, R.G. (1972). *Human engineering guide to equipment design*. Washington, DC: US Government Printing Office

WOODSON, W.E. (1981). *Human factors design handbook*. New York: McGraw-Hill

Chapter 6

Anthropometry and the design of workplaces

In this chapter we go beyond the layout of panels and consoles, and consider the design of the whole workspace. After a discussion of basic anthropometry, procedures are described for designing and evaluating the workspace. The chapter concludes with a discussion of seating.

Adapting

There are many tasks which oblige people to remain sitting or standing in a fixed position for long periods. Activities such as machining, industrial inspection, dentistry, driving, or just sitting at a desk or computer terminal are typical. The posture adopted by the person is determined by the need to reach controls, to keep the feet on pedals, or to keep the eyes in positions from which the task can be seen. When the task is very dangerous or demanding, as it might be for an astronaut or a pilot (Fig 6.1) the consequences of making things too difficult for the operator are serious and may be life threatening for a large number of people. In such cases, great efforts are made to minimise the discomfort and difficulty of reaching for controls and reading displays. In many tasks, however, when the consequences of error are neither as serious nor as obvious, people are often expected to adapt to a working posture, even though this may cause discomfort and difficulty in the first instance. The ability of people to adapt themselves to difficult situations, and their willingness to accept the challenge of tasks that are more difficult than they need be, should not blind us to the costs of adaptation. Among these costs are

- injuries and strains from bad working postures,
- less spare capacity to deal with emergencies,
- greater probability of accidents,
- greater probability of error.

Often these costs are accepted as inevitable: people get used to unsuitable working arrangements and are unaware of the need to change even when they could benefit from it. Thus people will sit in unsuitable chairs for long periods of time, working at a table whose height is not properly related to either the person or the chair. They will tolerate having to stretch uncomfortably to reach cupboard handles, or adopt uncomfortable postures in

Figure 6.1 It is easy to see that there could be high penalties for mistakes in the layout of a pilot's workspace. There are many seemingly less critical situations in which careful consideration of workspace design would bring benefits in increased safety, higher productivity, and reduced strain for the operator.

order to make repairs to their washing machines or cars. It is quite true that some degree of adaptation is acceptable and tolerable; if it were not, every piece of equipment would have to be fitted exactly to each person who uses it, and even casual observation shows that this is rarely necessary. However, beyond a certain point, adaptation may have adverse consequences on the person, such as those listed above, and in extreme cases no amount of adaptation can resolve the difference between the characteristics of the user and those of the machine. Under these circumstances the machine or equipment is unusable.

It is necessary to foresee difficulties of posture, reach and visibility early in the design process to make realistic and effective changes. It is relatively easy to spot faults in workplace layout when the equipment and furniture is in use, but by then it is usually too late to make alterations, and the operator is required to do all the adapting. The difficulty of predicting faults in the layout of a workplace before the equipment has been made or selected, and installed, is that the designer's own experience or knowledge will not provide enough information about the user's requirements. Time and facilities must be allowed for a systematic search for the following kinds of information:

- an analysis of the operations that make up the task;
- body sizes of the people who will carry out the operations;

• reaching and seeing requirements for adequate human performance;
• the total space that could be made available to the operator for all feasible arrangements of the equipment.

In the following sections we discuss human body size, methods of using body size data in design and evaluating the solutions, and, as an illustration, apply these principles to the design of seating.

Body sizes

People vary not only in their height but also in their proportions. Two people of the same height and sex are almost certain to differ in arm or leg length, or sitting height, or hand size, or any body dimension. By 'body size' is meant, therefore, not just height but any body measurement which is important for the equipment or workspace being designed. It is a mistake, also, to think of an 'average adult', or even 'average male' and 'average female': whilst someone who is tall is likely to have long legs and long arms, the correlation between any two body dimensions is not perfect. Thus it is common for a person of, say, average height to have arms and legs that are not of average length. The 'average man' may exist on paper, but is very uncommon on the hoof.

To design a workspace properly, the range of sizes of the anticipated user population must be known. The users of a piece of equipment may form a large group, such as 'all men' (for example, building workers) or 'all men, women, and older teenagers' (for example, private car drivers) or they may be a more restricted group, such as 'all children under the age of 12 years' (for example, users of primary school furniture). Knowledge of the average body dimensions of the group of users is not sufficient; the distribution and range of sizes within the group must be known or estimated. Fortunately, it has been shown that in the case of many dimensions, this distribution is known and can be closely approximated by a known mathematical formulation. Fig 6.2 shows this shape, called a 'normal' or 'Gaussian' distribution. It can be seen that most people in a group are near the average for the group, but that a sizeable proportion are appreciably above or below the average, and a few people will be far from the average. The total range of variation may be large compared with the designer's

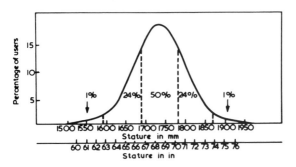

Figure 6.2 Distribution of heights of a user population.

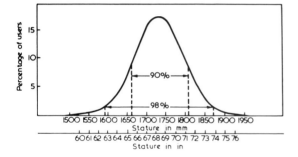

Figure 6.3 90% of this same population vary in height by only 150 mm (6 in), 98% vary by 280 mm (11 in), and 100% vary by a much larger but unknown amount.

room for manoeuvre, and it may be impossible to accommodate all users in comfort. For this reason, it is common in ergonomics solutions to aim to cater for 90% of the user population, and to exclude the 5% furthest above and the 5% furthest below the average, as shown in Fig 6.3. On some occasions, even this is impossible, and the designer may be forced to exclude a large proportion. There are also cases where the exclusion of a proportion of the population is not symmetrical about the average; to take a trivial example, the height of a doorway excludes only those people who are inordinately tall, and not those who are very short. On the other hand, a wall-mounted kitchen cupboard will cause difficulty to short people, and not to tall people. In general, tasks that involve reaching may cause problems for relatively short people, and those that involve fitting into spaces will cause problems for tall people (Fig 6.4).

It is important to notice the difference between designing for a restricted population and designing for the population as a whole. If equipment fits, say, 95% of adult males, it could fail to fit up to 30% of adult females. Equipment designed for 95% of adult females may suit only 60% of adult males. The precision needed in the layout of a workspace for a range of body sizes rather than for a single person is shown in Fig 6.5. A fairly wide

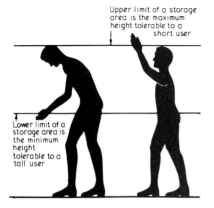

Figure 6.4 Some dimensions should be arrived at by relating the requirements to likely extremes in body sizes among the user population.

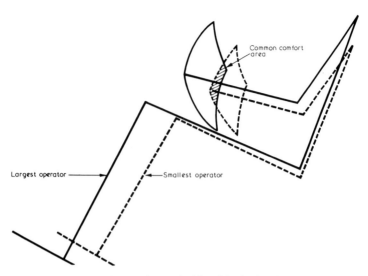

Figure 6.5 The areas that can be reached by all body sizes in a user population are far smaller than the areas that can be reached by one person. The common comfort area for gripping a steering wheel is indicated by the shaded area.

range of positions for any one piece of equipment can usually be tolerated without discomfort by one size of user, as indicated by the comfort zone for the position of hand controls in the diagram. The tolerable range for a person of a different size may be equally large, but these ranges may not coincide. As the figure shows, there is often only a small overlap, and sometimes there may be no overlap at all. In this case, it may be necessary to make the equipment in several sizes, or to allow it to be adjustable.

Since the overlap, if any, may be very small, measurement rather than common-sense judgement is required to locate it. There is a large quantity of anthropometric data available, and this will frequently serve the designer in the initial specification of dimensions for a piece of equipment or a workspace. Fig 6.6 gives a sample of such tabulated data, and other sources are listed in the references at the end of the chapter. However, four important points must be made about the use of such published data, as follows.

(1) *Reference population.* An anthropometric survey is expensive and time consuming to conduct; for this reason, most are done with specific aims in mind, rather than general ones. The armed services and other uniformed organisations collect much anthropometric data from their personnel in order to provide uniforms and to design specialised equipment. As a result, a large proportion of published data is based on military populations, whose members are generally younger, taller, and fitter than the general population. Other data sources may refer to ethnic and national populations different from the one of interest, and there are known differences between the dimensions of different races and nationalities. For these reasons, care is needed in the use of published data, in order to avoid ascribing to one population the dimensions of another; some correction to the figures may be necessary.

Percentages of the population with dimensions less than those given below

	Men 5%	50%	95%	Women 5%	50%	95%
Stature	1625	1740	1855	1505	1610	1710
A back of knee — floor	400	440	480	380	415	450
B back of knee — buttock	440	495	550	430	480	535
C elbow — seat height	190	240	285	185	225	265
D shoulder — seat height	545	600	655	510	565	615
E sitting height	850	910	970	790	845	900
F hip breadth	315	360	400	320	375	430
G elbow breadth	390	450	510	300	385	475
H biacromial breadth	365	400	440	325	355	385

Estimated nude measurements of the British population between the ages of 19 and 65.
Dimensions are in millimetres.

Source: Pheasant ST (1984) 'Anthropometrics — an introduction for schools and colleges'
(London: BSI).

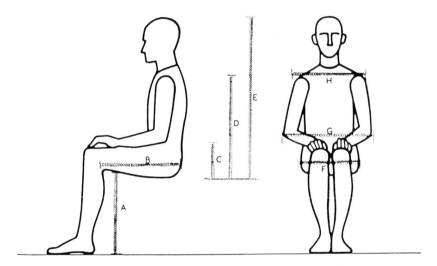

Figure 6.6 Anthropometric dimensions for seating (after Pheasant 1984).

(2) *Changes over time.* It is known that the dimensions of a population change over time: as a result of improvements in economic conditions, health care and diet, a population tends to get taller. The rate of change depends on the quality of these factors and on the conditions prevailing at the start of a time period. Thus, in western economies, where the standard of living has been relatively high for many years, the secular change in body size is now smaller than it used to be. The change is more marked in countries where improvements in living standards are relatively recent. Since secular change in body size can be as much as 1 cm per decade, care should be taken when using data that were collected some time ago. The cautious designer will also bear in mind that the period between the collection of data and its eventual publication may extend to several years.

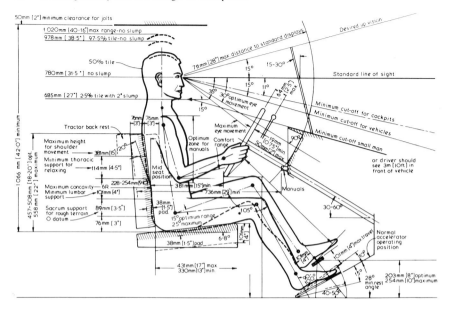

Figure 6.7. An 'average' male figure, used as the basis for a series of recommendations for workspaces and equipment.

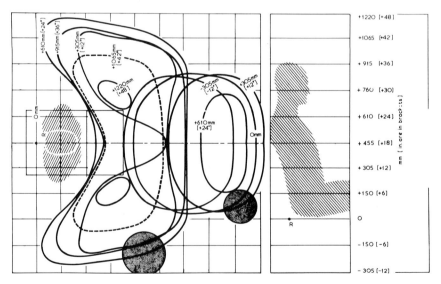

Figure 6.8 The space which can be reached by a seated operator while strapped into an aircraft seat has been very carefully worked out by the US Air Force. The resulting contour map of the three-dimensional reachable workspace shows very clearly that the length of reach depends on direction of reach. The two-dimensional character of drawing board layouts and profile diagrams of body and reach make it easy to overlook this point.

(3) *Nature of the measurement.* For the purposes of standardisation, most anthropometric data are collected from unclothed and unshod volunteers. Whilst this gives a reliable baseline, the designer must, when specifying a workspace or piece of equipment, make allowances for clothing. For example, a control that can be operated by the bare hand may be too small for operation by a gloved hand; foot pedals that have been designed on the basis of 'unshod' data may be very difficult to use by someone wearing shoes, particularly if they have high heels; and the designer of escape hatches must remember that those using them may be encumbered with protective equipment such as padded coats and life-jackets.

(4) *Static and dynamic anthropometry.* The length of a person's arm will limit the distance that he or she can reach. However, the distance that can be reached will be greater than the length of the arm, because reaching can involve movement of the shoulder and the trunk. On the other hand, the distance that can be reached to operate a control which is grasped by the whole hand will be less than that for a control which is operated by the fingertips. In general, static anthropometric measures refer to the actual sizes of the body components; dynamic or functional measures refer to the ability of the body to perform certain tasks within certain distances, spaces, or enclosures. The functional dimension will depend on the task being performed. Some anthropometric data are presented in what amounts to a functional form: Figs. 6.7 and 6.8 show recommended distances and dimensions for the location of controls and displays for a motor car and for the controls in an aircraft. However, because functional data are so task-specific, the designer should remember that small differences in the task, such as in the amount of force required on a control lever, can call for large differences in posture and space requirements. Recommended equipment sizes should only be used when it is quite clear that no special features of

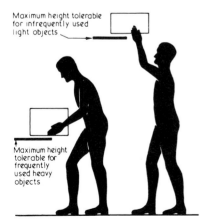

Maximum height tolerable for infrequently used light objects

Maximum height tolerable for frequently used heavy objects

Figure 6.9 The acceptable limits of reaching are influenced not only by body size and the forces that have to be exerted but also by frequency of the action concerned. For instance, heavy objects should be stored within a narrow range of heights close to the waist, whereas light objects may be stored at any height between knee and shoulder. These limits can be extended if the objects are infrequently used.

the task in question have been overlooked. It should also be borne in mind that there is a difference between the distance that can be reached comfortably and frequently, and that which can be reached, if only occasionally, with some effort (Fig 6.9).

Procedures for designing equipment and workspaces

A well-laid-out workspace, or a well-designed piece of equipment, is one in which the operator can see and reach quickly and easily all the items of equipment necessary for successful completion of the tasks. The operator should also be able to occupy the workspace or use the equipment for periods of time commensurate with this, in such a posture or postures that there is no discomfort or strain. Some tasks are more complicated than they first appear, and can involve many reaching and seeing requirements that are difficult to satisfy simultaneously. Displays and controls may be so numerous that only a few of them may be placed in the most accessible positions. Others may have to be placed in locations that are only just within the reaching and seeing ranges of some users. In many cases, difficulties of this sort mean that the final solution is not ideal from an ergonomics point of view, and a compromise solution must often be reached. It is the job of the ergonomist to ensure that this compromise is the best possible, and that it causes the user as little inconvenience and discomfort as possible. The design process whereby this may be achieved can be considered as comprising several stages. They are described below.

Task analysis and statement of activities

The first stage is to obtain a detailed analysis of all the actions that the operator has to carry out, and the equipment that will be involved in this. This analysis should be started before engineering and production decisions have limited the number of positions in which any item of equipment can be placed, and before general arrangement drawings have been started. There are formidable difficulties which often prevent this systematic consideration of workspace and equipment layout at a sufficiently early stage in design, but considerable benefits will be obtained when these difficulties are overcome. Significant improvements are unlikely to occur unless the design group investigates operator requirements at the start, and refrains from the usual practice of developing new equipment around a preconceived or traditional operator position and posture.

A useful means of collecting and checking the information required to determine workspace layout is shown in Fig 6.10. All the important links between operator and equipment, and between one item of equipment and another, are found by checking for a possible interaction between every pair of items listed. They are indicated by spots on the chart. Fig 6.11 shows a workplace that might be described by this chart. A checklist, such as that shown in Table 6.1, can be used to obtain a description of each of the operator requirements.

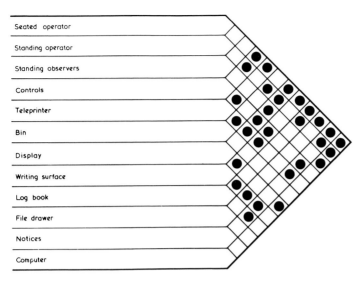

Figure 6.10 A useful way of checking workspace requirements. Each spot on the chart denotes a reaching or seeing requirement that will affect the layout of the workspace.

Figure 6.11 A situation in which the workspace requirements are similar to those set out in the chart in Fig 6.10.

Table 6.1 A checklist for describing each of the user's requirements

1 What are the user's purposes or objectives?
2 By what actions will the user attempt to achieve these objectives?
3 Which actions are particularly important, and which are of little importance? (Importance can be assessed by the probability of great or small consequences of failure to carry out each action.)
4 Which actions require continuous vision of displays or controls, and which actions require only occasional glances?
5 Which actions require simultaneous vision of two or more items?
6 What is the duration of each action?
7 What is the frequency of each action?
8 Which body measurements are critical for each action?
9 Which actions are likely to be fatiguing?
10 Which actions call for either the maximum forces the muscles concerned can exert, or for a particularly light touch?
11 Which actions require an awkward grip or posture that greatly reduces the force that can be exerted or the distance that can be reached?
12 Which actions are in awkward positions or directions in relation to the body?
13 What degrees of body motion are compatible with carrying out the actions with the required efficiency and without noticeable discomfort?
14 Will the users be unfamiliar with the actions required, or highly skilled in carrying them out?
15 Will a large proportion of users be encountering new equipment for the first time, and are they likely to compare it unfavourably with equipment with which they have become familiar through long experience?
16 Will the users expect, or be very appreciative of, great comfort and convenience, or will they be willing to tolerate considerable discomfort and inconvenience?

It may also be important to allow space in a work area for trainees, visitors, supervisors, assistants, and other people. In such cases as computer workstations, drafting units, and medical equipment, it may be necessary to enable other people to see what is going on without interfering with the main operator and the task, and without having to adopt awkward postures in order to do this. When several people work together in a large system or process, there may be requirements of visibility, hearing distances, timing of actions, and signalling by gesture, which can be greatly facilitated by good layout. Tasks such as controlling cranes, rolling mills, and the control of remote processes such as nuclear power stations can pose difficult problems of communication near the limits of human hearing and vision. In these cases, an analysis can be carried out to define exactly the network of messages and actions involved in the task, and the points where the unaided operator can most usefully be helped by aids such as telephone links, extra VDU screens, and closed circuit television. The many questions that are posed by such systematic methods of seeking design information can be answered in the following ways:

• observation and measurement of the activities of people using either similar equipment, or in a simulator or mockup of the proposed design;
• pilot trials in which members of the design group go through the actions involved;
• consultation with operators who have experience of similar tasks.

It is important that the task analysis is completed before any decisions are taken concerning the general form of the workspace: for example, before it has been decided whether the operator shall sit or stand or be free to do either.

Pre-testing the workspace

When all the questions of body size, reach, visibility, and task have been examined, it is necessary to make some kind of simulation to assess how they fit together as a complete workspace. There are three basic ways in which this can be done, as follows.

Models. These may be two-dimensional (drawing board renderings of the workspace with scale manikins placed over the drawing) or three-dimensional (models made from simple materials such as cardboard or plywood). This method is quick and relatively easy, but is rather crude and may not allow for the variation in comfort tolerance that occurs with different actions, postures, and kinds of task; however, it is a useful first step and can be particularly valuable in illustrating to the eventual user the

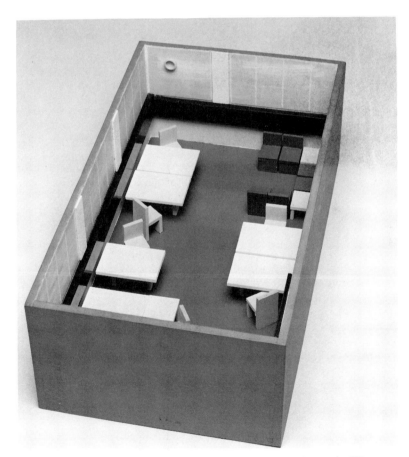

Figure 6.12 A wooden model of a data preparation room, used to study different arrangements of equipment and facilities.

general form of the solution being proposed. Fig 6.12 shows a simple scale model, made from plywood and balsa, of a data preparation room containing people, computers, workstations, and other furniture. It was constructed so as to allow the data preparation personnel themselves to explore different room layouts without having to move the actual furniture around.

Figure 6.13 A mockup used for simulating driving postures in trucks. One of a series of fitting trials devised by A. Wisner.

Simulations. Full size three-dimensional simulations of equipment and workspaces are clearly more expensive and time consuming to build than models, but they have the considerable advantage of allowing the user directly to experience the facility being designed, and thus for formal trials to be executed with a range of users. Simulations can, however, vary in sophistication, and it is usually not too difficult to create a reasonable simulation without incurring great expense, provided it is remembered that sophistication and realism are related to each other. Furthermore, a simulation may be made of only a part of a workspace, where, for instance, particular problems are likely to arise or where certain dimensions are critical. Fig 6.13 shows a simulator used for the study of driving postures, which is systematically adjusted to find the maximum and minimum tolerable positions for each item of equipment for human subjects representing the range of body sizes of the expected users. The tolerable ranges of each equipment dimension for a range of subjects are recorded in diagrams, an

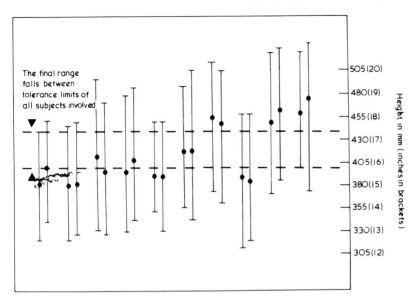

Figure 6.14 The tolerance ranges for all subjects for one dimension are charted together. If these ranges overlap, it is possible to select a narrow final range within the tolerance limits of all subjects.

example of which is shown in Fig 6.14. In this example it can be seen that there is an overlap which falls within the tolerance ranges for all subjects. Fig 6.15 shows a simple fitting trial using improvised materials that happen to be at hand; this may be quite acceptable if the problem is a simple one, or if the consequences of a mismatch between user and equipment are small. Fig 6.16 shows a more sophisticated simulation of parts of the passenger compartment of a motor car; many aspects of this model were

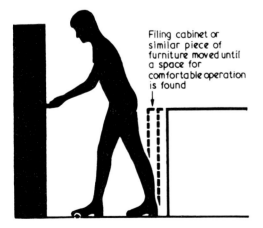

Figure 6.15 Simplified fitting trials can be carried out by rearranging office furniture and equipment to simulate the significant dimensions, adjusting them over a suitable range.

Figure 6.16 A full size, adjustable simulation of a motor car, used to assess vehicle design for easy access and use by disabled people.

adjustable, and it was used to assess the accessibility of cars by disabled people, by means of a user trial.

Computer-aided design. Computers are being used increasingly to explore quickly and easily the feasibility of various solutions to workspace design problems. With appropriate software, the designer can save much time and effort in two-dimensional renderings and in three-dimensional model making, by taking account of critical dimensions and requirements, developing solutions on the computer screen, and rejecting those solutions which do not satisfy the basic requirements. The computer-generated models can be represented in two or three dimensions, and, once developed, can be enlarged, reduced, or rotated, and can be presented as though viewed from different positions within the model. This allows the evaluation of vision requirements as well as body size problems. Components of the model can be changed easily to assess alternative solutions. Fig 6.17 shows some output from one CAD system, known as SAMMIE (System for Aiding Man–Machine Interaction Evaluation) which, in addition to showing the actual workspace and equipment, allows the designer to place a man model in the workspace, in any of a number of postures, to see whether an acceptable fit has been achieved.

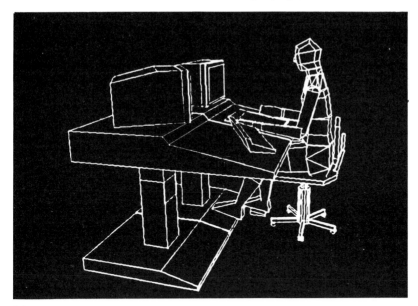

(a)

(b)

Figure 6.17(a). Output from the computer-aided design system SAMMIE, allowing the designer to assess the fit between user, equipment, and workspace. (b) The final product, based on the studies made with the SAMMIE system. (Courtesy Dr J.M. Porter, Lough-borough University)

The design of seating

With continuing technological advances, people at work are progressively being relieved of the need to generate force and power themselves. Instead, they control force- and power-generating equipment by means of controls and displays, or monitor the behaviour of such equipment, intervening in the process only when some corrective action is required. In addition, more and more people are using computers and computer-based equipment in offices and similar environments. The result of these developments is that many people remain seated for a large part of the day, whether they are inspecting goods, operating computers, or using small powered tools. There is thus a considerable interest in the design of seating, and in identifying those features of a seat which contribute significantly to the enhancement of its comfort and efficiency.

Before discussing some of the main features of seat design, it should be emphasised that no seat, however carefully designed, can of itself ensure overall comfort and efficiency for long periods of time. This is because the design of the seat should always be made in relation to other equipment used by the sitter, and the nature and duration of the tasks performed. The human body is not designed to stay in a seated position for long periods of time, and requires occasional relief from this position as well as the freedom to shift position slightly during the time seated. There have been many reports and investigations of the problems of stress and strain experienced by typists and computer operators: good seating design can help to reduce the number and severity of these problems, but it is also vital to consider the other equipment in the workplace (in order to maintain a good posture) and the design of work/rest schedules to allow some change from continuous sitting.

The purpose of seating

The main purpose of a seat is not just to take the weight off the feet, but also to support the sitter so that a stable posture can be maintained which allows those muscles not directly involved in the task to be relaxed. The seat should be designed to minimise discomfort due to unnecessary pressure on the underside of the thighs, or to the restriction of blood supply to the buttocks because of an unsuitable distribution of the sitter's weight. It should also support the spine to minimise strain on the spinal vertebrae and the muscles in the shoulders, back, and pelvis which hold the spine in its normal shape. Furthermore, as mentioned above, a range of postures needs to be possible, since prolonged sitting in one position leads to discomfort.

The sitter can often do much to reduce the worst effects of poor seating by adopting some postures and avoiding others, although this necessarily incurs costs in effort, comfort, or efficiency. For example, seated people spend much of the time with their legs crossed, leaning with their arms on a table or on an arm rest. Crossing the legs tends to lock the joints and thus stabilises the various parts of the body, although pressure on the ischial tuberosities (the weight-bearing parts of the buttocks) becomes unequally distributed and can lead to discomfort (Fig 6.18). The designer can help to

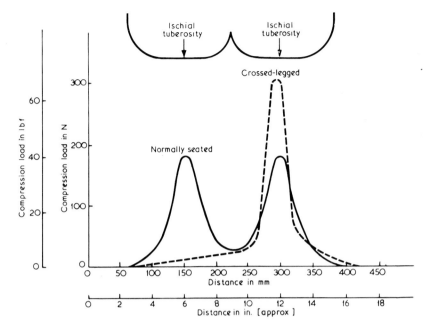

Figure 6.18 Pressure distribution pattern on buttocks during normal and cross-legged sitting.

reduce instability by proportioning the seat properly, and providing trunk supports and back rests at the right points.

The criteria of good support and maximum comfort may not indicate the same solution. A hard seat, properly contoured, will provide good support, but unless this contouring is pronounced, the seat will become uncomfortable after a while, because the body weight will be taken by only a small part of the body surface. Yet a pronounced contour, although it may distribute the weight over a wider area, may restrict movement, and itself will lead to discomfort. If we attempt to solve this problem by cushioning the seat surface, essential support to the body may be lost, and the work of stabilising the body falls once more to the muscles. Any practical solution, therefore, will be a compromise between support and comfort.

Seats, posture, and task performance

Working at a table or bench, the seated person acts literally as a link between seat and task, and efficiency will obviously depend on the layout of the workplace and the seat (Fig 6.19). It has been shown that the position of the elbow, and the distance from the eye to the task, are crucial for many perceptual–motor tasks, such as typing. Such tasks are best carried out when the work surface is at elbow height or just lower, and the angle formed at the elbow is 90° or more.

A common problem is the lack of knee and leg room which prevents the person from coming close enough to the task. Besides causing discomfort

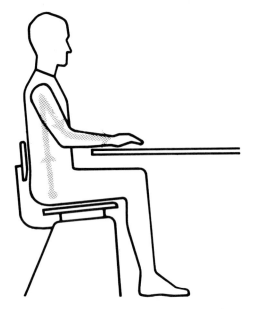

Figure 6.19 The body of a seated person is a flexible link between seat and workpiece. If the two are in proper relation to each other, work can be performed efficiently.

to the legs, this can mean that the arms must be extended to an uncomfortable extent, and the end result is a needlessly fatiguing posture in which the task is carried out inefficiently.

It is likely that a number of tasks will be carried out at a given table or workplace. For example, a kitchen table may be used for eating, food preparation, writing, reading, and a number of other activities. A workbench in a factory may be used for assembly, inspection, testing, and so forth. Because these different tasks may have different visual, manual force, and manual skill requirements, it may be difficult to specify one seat–work–surface relationship that satisfies them all. In addition, some of the tasks may be performed by a standing person rather than one in a seated position—indeed, this may be desirable, to allow for a change of posture over a period of time. In such cases, a compromise may have to be made, or the seat and work surface may need to be adjustable, with the likely increase in cost that this will entail. In some cases, seats can be fitted with footrests so that a high work surface can be tolerated without the person's legs being left unsupported.

Chair dimensions

We now consider, as an example, the design of chairs for use when the person sits upright at a table or bench, performing tasks which do not require the application of large forces or the use of very specialised equipment. These tasks may include reading, writing, typing, light assembly, and eating. Some of the recommendations below would also, however, apply to the design of other types of seating. The recommendations are not exhaustive but are used to illustrate the main features of a chair of this design.

Fig 6.6 shows the important human dimensions for chair design, and their distribution in the population of adults. The columns of figures for

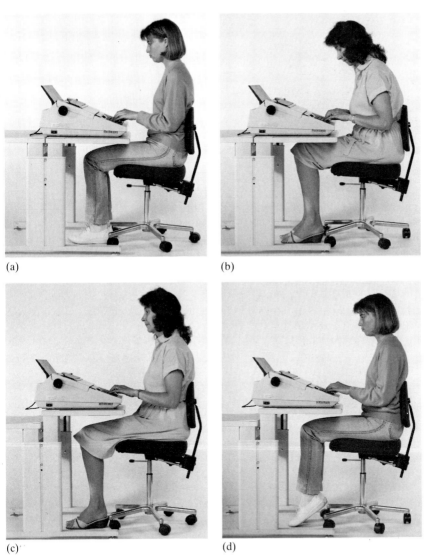

(a)　　　　　　　　　　　　(b)

(c)　　　　　　　　　　　　(d)

Figure 6.20(a) This typist is relatively short (1626 mm stature) and needs both the table and chair seat to be low in order to sit comfortably. (b) This typist is relatively tall (1702 mm stature). Her preferred seat height is 50 mm higher than that for the shorter typist, and the preferred table height is 70 mm higher. (c) The tall typist using a chair and table setting suitable for the shorter typist finds that there is insufficient knee room, and that she must lean her head and shoulders forward in order to see the work. (d) When the shorter typist uses a chair and table setting suitable for the taller typist, she is not able to place her feet comfortably on the floor.

each sex show the value of the dimension below which the given percentage of people will lie. Thus 5% of adult males will be 1625 mm or less in height. The figures are for unclothed people, so an allowance must be made for clothing, particularly for shoes. It is also necessary to make allowances for the effect of cushioning in the chair, since both the effective seat height and the shape of the seat surface will be changed when a person sits on it.

Seat height. The seat height should not be greater than the length of the lower leg measured from the floor to the inside of the knee bent at a right angle (Fig 6.20). If it is higher, there will be excessive pressure on the underside of the thigh. Among adults, this dimension ranges from about 380 mm to 480 mm. 25 mm should be added to this to account for shoes and the upholstery used. A height of 430 mm is often recommended for the seat surface: this allows most men to sit comfortably but can be too high for some women. If it is impracticable to provide an adjustable seat height, it is better to choose one near the lower end of the range, so as to suit most people. Tall people will be able to use the seat without serious discomfort, although their thighs will have less support than is desirable. It may also be a little more difficult to get up from a low seat.

Seat depth. This should be less than the distance from the back of the buttocks to the inside of the calf, to allow enough space to prevent the edge of the seat pressing into the back of the calf. If the seat is too deep, the sitter moves forward to relieve this pressure, and thus loses the support of the backrest. If it is too shallow, part of the thigh will be unsupported, although this may not be as severe a problem as the first. A depth of about 380 mm is usually recommended.

Seat width. This is determined by the need to accommodate the hips and lower trunk. A width of 410 mm will fit all but the broadest person, although 50 mm should be added to this to allow for clothing and the contents of pockets. Maximum widths are likely to be constrained by space requirements at the workplace, particularly if seats are placed next to each other in a row. If the chair has armrests, these should be at least 490 mm apart. Too narrow a seat will restrict movement and changes in posture.

Arm rests. Arm rests can restrict movement, but provide lateral support for the body as well as for the arms, and can be used as leverage points for getting in and out of the chair. The height of an arm rest depends on the distance between the elbow and the seat surface. The recommended value is about 200 mm above the compressed seat surface.

Back rest. This is a very difficult component to design, and its relation to all other parts of the seat is critical. It should be high enough to support the lumbar region (the small of the back), which extends from about 125 mm to about 200 mm above the compressed seat surface. Lumbar supports are often shaped so as to induce a curve in the spine (Fig 6.21), which encourages good posture and minimises fatigue. The back rest can extend above the lumbar region to support the shoulders, although this can restrict movement of the body. A back rest may also be contoured across its surface, so as to provide lateral body support. Most people are comfortable when leaning slightly back, so that the seat surface and the back rest form certain angles to themselves and to the floor. The angle between the

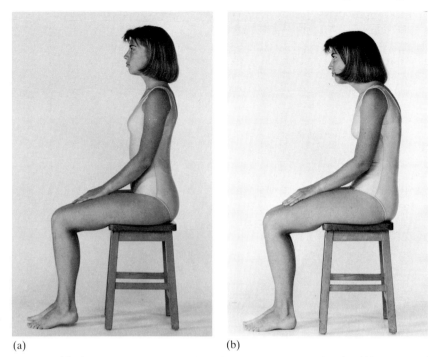

(a)   (b)

Figure 6.2(a) The natural curve in the spine of a seated position, which should be supported and maintained by a lumbar backrest. (b) An undesirable posture in which spinal curvature is not maintained.

compressed seat surface and the back rest should not be less than 95°. The compressed surface of the seat should either be horizontal or should slope back by up to about 5°, to prevent the sitter from sliding off the seat. A seat surface with a moderately rough texture can help prevent the sitter from sliding forward, although this should not be so rough as to make minor changes in position difficult to achieve. It should be added that, following research first published in 1970 in Scandinavia, and in 1976 in the UK, a large number of designers, mainly in Scandinavia but latterly elsewhere, advocate a seat which is higher than the dimensions given above, and which has a forward-sloping seat surface. The user of a chair of this design adopts a posture in which the angle between the trunk and the thighs is relatively large, and in which more of the body weight is taken by the feet. This design is said to be more comfortable than the conventional seat design, and beneficial for the user because the natural curvature of the spine is maintained (Fig. 6.22).

Chair evaluation

Whilst the recommendations given above, and other similar ones, are essential for the basic specification of the chair, the prototype version must be evaluated under actual usage conditions or, if this is not possible, in a

Figure 6.22 Bent-posture work with tilting seat and inclining desk-top (after Mandal 1976).

simulation of these conditions. To do this, people are selected representing different groups of the population in terms of various critical body dimensions. The physical fit of the chair to these people would be assessed when some task is being carried out, as a check on the basic data used. In addition, a systematic study of perceived comfort over a period of time may be made, using subjective scales of the comfort of individual body components as well as that of the body as a whole. A record may also be made of the postures adopted, and the extent to which these change over time: it can be argued that a sitter who changes posture frequently is less comfortable than one who does so only occasionally.

Summary of design recommendations

(1) The feet should rest on the floor, or a firm and stable footrest should be provided.
(2) Seat height should be no greater than the lower leg length. If people of widely varying heights are to use the chair, seat height should be adjustable, and the adjustment should be easy to make.
(3) The seat surface should be horizontal, or should slope backwards by up to 5°.

(4) The back rest should be at an angle of at least 95° to the seat surface.

(5) Seat texture should be enough to prevent sliding, but not so rough as to make minor movement difficult.

(6) The table or work surface should be no higher than the height of the elbow to the floor, for a seated person.

(7) It is better to reduce the height of a work surface rather than raise the height of a chair.

Further reading

DIFFRIENT, N., TILLEY, A.R., and BARDAGJY, J.C. (1974). *Humanscale 1/2/3*. Cambridge, Mass.: MIT Press

DIFFRIENT, N., TILLEY, A.R., and HARMAN, D. (1981). *Humanscale 7/8/9*. Cambridge, Mass.: MIT Press

MANDAL, A.C. (1976). *Ergonomics*, **19**, 2, 157–164. Work-chair with tilting seat

PANERO, J. and ZELNIK, M. (1979). *Human dimension and interior space*. London: Architectural Press

PHEASANT, S.T. (1984). *Anthropometrics: an introduction for schools and colleges*. London: BSI

PHEASANT, S.T. (1986). *Bodyspace*. London: Taylor and Francis

ROEBUCK, J.A., KROEMER, K.H.E., and THOMSON, W.G. (1975). *Engineering anthropometry methods*. New York: McGraw-Hill

SINGLETON, W.T. (1982). *The body at work—biological ergonomics*. Cambridge: CUP

Chapter 7

The environment—climatic factors

In this chapter we discuss the way in which the body maintains a constant temperature, and the various means of heat transfer. Factors affecting how hot or cold a person may feel are detailed, with a discussion on suitable thermal conditions. Tasks carried out in extremes of temperature are also dealt with.

Sizing up the problem

Studies of conditions in industries such as coalmining, steel, textiles and laundries, as well as in offices, have shown that poor ventilation, and temperatures that are too high or too low, result in a loss of efficiency, discontent, and increased rates of accident and sickness. They can also affect the supply of labour, since people have come to expect a higher standard of comfort than in the past, and if this is not provided they may go elsewhere.

What is necessary to ensure a satisfactory 'indoor climate' for various tasks? This chapter addresses the question by considering how the temperature of the body is controlled, how heat travels, what factors are important, for example temperature, humidity and movement of air, what are the best conditions to aim at, and how to cope with extremes of temperature.

These factors are an important part of ergonomics. The ergonomist, as well as specifying the hardware that people use to carry out tasks, also defines the environment in which the task is done so that the whole user/task/environment system is optimised. Neglecting any of these components leads to an inefficient solution which may require an unacceptable or impossible degree of adaptation on the part of the user (Fig 7.1).

Body temperature regulation

To understand why a particular environment feels too hot or too cold instead of just comfortable, we need to know something of how the human body works.

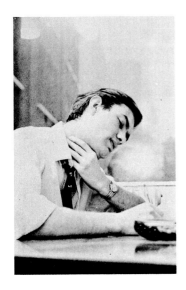

Figure 7.1 Few people would choose to live in a greenhouse all the year round, yet the indoor climate in this modern office block is not very different.

Heat is continuously generated deep inside the body by chemical processes, known as metabolism, which ultimately involve the oxidisation of the food we eat by the oxygen in the air we breathe. Even when we are lying quite still or asleep and the body is only 'ticking over', metabolic heat is produced at a rate equivalent to the power consumption of a 60-watt electric light bulb. During physical work the muscles of the body convert only about 20% of the chemical energy used into mechanical power, and the remaining 80% appears as heat. An athlete in action can produce as much heat as a 1-kilowatt electric fire. All the heat generated in the deep tissues must be brought by the bloodstream to the skin surface where it is dissipated to the air. Without this dissipation, the human would die.

In a healthy person, the temperature under the tongue is usually about 37°C (98.6°F). There are small differences between one individual and another, and within one person there is a cyclical rise and fall in temperature over 24 hours. In general, however, the temperature in the deeper tissues of the body is held constant. This constancy is achieved by continually varying the rate of blood flow to the body surface, especially in the head and the limbs. When the deep body temperature rises above normal, the blood vessels near the skin dilate, and more blood, carrying heat from the deeper tissues, passes through them. In cold conditions the surface blood vessels contract so that the heat in the deep tissues is conserved.

If the air temperature is so high that the difference in temperature between the skin and the air is small, or if the body is producing too much heat by physical exertion, insufficient heat is lost by simple convection from the skin to the air, and the body temperature begins to rise. This stimulates the sweat glands, and the correct body temperature is then restored by the release of sweat, which, on evaporating, draws heat from the body surface. In very hot conditions as much as 1 litre of sweat is released each hour, and all this fluid must be replaced by means of drinking if dehydration is to be avoided. It is wise to remember that thirst is not a good guide to the amount of fluid needed, and people should be encouraged to drink more fluid than they think they want. Alcohol should be avoided since, although it is a fluid, it also has a diuretic effect—that of causing the body to release fluid via urine—and so is counterproductive. Some salt is lost in sweat but, in general, it is not necessary to take extra salt unless the exposure to heat is very intense and prolonged. Salt is vital to the welfare of the body, and people who work unprotected for long periods in very hot conditions sometimes suffer from a salt deficiency known as 'stoker's cramp', because they lose more salt in sweat than they are eating in their food.

If the body is repeatedly exposed to hot conditions, it becomes acclimatised and is more efficient in getting rid of heat. The acclimatisation period may be as short as a week, under continuous exposure. One of the most important changes is an increase in the capacity to release sweat, which can quite easily double. Other important changes are an increase in the amount of blood pumped by the heart through the body surface, and, in general, a more prompt response by all the mechanisms promoting loss of heat from the body. These changes enable a person to survive in conditions which would otherwise cause a collapse. Nevertheless, hot conditions impose an undesirable stress on even a fully acclimatised person, and efficiency and wellbeing would be improved if the environment could be changed.

The body reacts to cold conditions by restricting the blood supply to the body surface, particularly to the hands and feet, conserving the heat generated in the deep tissues. If this does not maintain the correct temperature, shivering begins, and this muscle activity produces heat. Both the speed and accuracy of typing, for example, are markedly impaired by quite moderate degrees of hand cooling (Fig 7.2).

The control of body temperature by varying the flow of blood to the

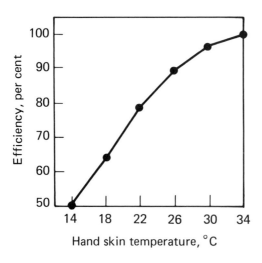

Figure 7.2 Hand temperature affects speed and accuracy.

surface is entirely automatic. We usually realise that we are too hot at about the same time that sweating starts.

The sweat itself may not be obvious because it may be evaporated as quickly as it is formed, but we still feel uncomfortably hot, and so open the window or remove some clothes. Even before we reach this point, the heat may reduce our efficiency at some tasks, and our power to concentrate. Similarly, if the air temperature is too low our manual dexterity may be impaired before we realise we are too cold.

Thus the aim should always be to provide conditions in which body temperature can be maintained by the fine control of small variations in the flow of blood to the surface.

How heat travels

Heat can travel into or away from the surface of the body by convection, conduction, radiation, and evaporation.

Convection of heat means its actual transfer by air (or liquid) in motion. Hot or cold objects in otherwise still air create their own convective air currents, because air expands with heating and therefore becomes lighter, or, if cooled, contracts and so becomes heavier. This is termed natural convection and is related to the temperature difference between the body or clothing surface and the air. If air (or the body) is moving, the heat can transfer due to forced convection. This is related to the relative velocity between the body and the air, as well as the temperature difference. Heat loss by convection can cause draughts in rooms with large windows. Air movements can also be caused by cooling fans for equipment such as visual display terminals.

Conduction of heat means its direct movement through a substance which is touching the human body. Thus, when standing on a cold floor, some heat is conducted directly from the feet through the soles of the shoes to the floor itself. Certain materials, particularly metals, are good heat conductors, while others, especially air itself, are bad conductors and therefore are useful insulators. Almost all the materials commonly used for thermal insulation depend for their efficiency on the air trapped in the material. Heat transfer between the body and surrounding objects will depend on the specific heat capacity, density, and thermal conductivity of the body and its surroundings. Typically, materials in direct contact with the body, such as air and fabrics, have a low thermal conductivity; heat transfer by conduction is negligible in this case, compared with heat transfer by convection and radiation. In some cases the body will come into contact with surfaces that have a relatively high or low temperature and relatively high thermal conductivity (for example, metals). This can cause discomfort, pain, and burns because of heat conduction.

Radiation of heat is the transfer of heat to or from the body by electro-magnetic waves. All materials emit these waves to some extent, and for any given material the intensity of the radiation depends simply on its surface temperature. In general, the electromagnetic waves are absorbed and converted back into heat when they fall on other solid objects, but some of those emitted from very hot sources like the sun have comparatively short wavelengths and are in the part of the spectrum visible to our eyes. They are able to pass through substances that we call transparent, such as glass, water, and air. The surfaces of some materials, especially highly polished metals, act as efficient reflectors of electromagnetic radiation, and thus reflect heat.

Evaporative cooling takes place when water is evaporated from a wet surface, because heat is absorbed in the process. The rate of cooling by this means depends on how much water vapour is already present in the air surrounding the wetted surface, on the temperature of the surface, and on the rate of air movement over it.

Desirable climatic conditions

Comfort levels

There are four important factors which determine whether we will feel hot, or cold, or comfortable:
(1) air temperature,
(2) radiant temperature,
(3) air humidity,
(4) rate of air movement.

Of these, air temperature is usually the most important. However, people differ considerably in their judgement of a comfortable air temperature, and this makes it very difficult to define an optimum level of air temperature for a given task. It is impossible to satisfy everybody all the time.

Fig 7.3 illustrates some instruments used to measure climatic features.

Air temperature
From observations on individuals doing light work in British factories, it has been found that the optimum air temperature is 18.3°C, and the comfort zone (over which not more than 1 person in 7 complains of actual discomfort) ranges from 15.6 to 20.0°C. Office workers and others in sedentary occupations usually require a higher temperature—between 19.4 and 22.8°C—because their muscles are not working sufficiently hard to generate enough body heat. For more active tasks the temperature should be lower, and for really heavy work 12.8 to 15.6°C is a suitable range. The air temperature should also be lower if the individual is exposed to sources of radiant heat.

Radiant temperature
Radiant heat levels should not be too high or too low for people carrying out light tasks. (Radiant heat is measured by means of a globe thermometer, comprising a thermometer whose bulb is contained inside a globe whose surface is matt black and which absorbs radiated heat.) The optimum level is 18.3°C and the comfort zone is from 16.7 to 20.0°C. It is important to shield people from radiant heat in those tasks involving high temperature processes, such as are found in industries such as steel and

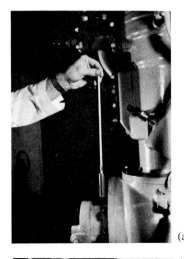

(a)

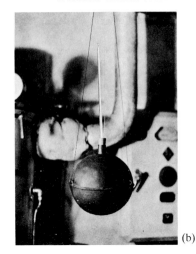

(b)

(c)

Figure 7.3 Examples of instruments used to measure climatic variables: (a) dry bulb thermometer for measuring air temperature; (b) globe thermometer, used in the measurement of radiant temperature; (c) whirling hygrometer, used in the measurement of relative humidity. Climatic variables can also be measured by means of electronic instruments.

glass making. Quite apart from the discomfort this exposure can cause, the body will start to sweat to maintain its temperature, and body fluid will be lost. In extreme cases, actual damage to the skin can occur (Fig 7.4).

Air humidity
Humidity has relatively little effect on thermal comfort at ordinary temperatures, but extremes are to be avoided, especially if the task in hand involves heavy physical work. Humidity is usually measured as a percentage of the moisture that would completely saturate the air at the existing temperature. This 'relative humidity' should not normally exceed 70%. Very low humidities may cause discomfort through drying of the nose and throat, particularly if the air temperature is very high, as in a desert. A very high humidity, combined with a high temperature, may be experienced in a hot, steamy bathroom. In less extreme cases, too high a humidity may be partly responsible for the sensations of stuffiness in a crowded and badly

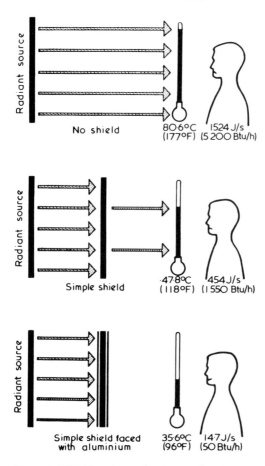

Figure 7.4 Shielding the worker from radiant heat can produce some dramatic benefits.

ventilated room. As the air temperature rises above the comfort zone, excessive humidity limits the rate at which sweat can be evaporated, making it more difficult for the body to regulate its heat.

Rate of air movement

Provided the air and radiant temperatures are correct, the ideal level of air movement is around 0.15 m/s (metres per second). This is just about the point at which the movement is perceptible. Above 0.51 m/s is usually regarded as 'very draughty', and much below 0.1 m/s as 'airless'.

The ability to detect small air movements is due to the temperature change in the skin, and the cooler the air the more easily is its movement detected. Indeed, this sensitivity to cold explains many of the complaints made about draughts. If the general heating in a room is improved, draughts become less obvious and less unpleasant even though the rate of air movement is unchanged. If the air temperature is above the comfort level, then air movements much in excess of 0.51 m/s can be very welcome because they assist in the exchange of heat between the body and the air.

It is often difficult to control air movement so as to produce ideal conditions, particularly when there are few windows, the ceiling is very low, the room is very large or small, or where there are large fluctuations in the number of people occupying the room. The problem can sometimes be solved by a fan or by an air-conditioning system.

A low-speed fan, with long blades, which is suspended from the ceiling and which is usually associated with living in the tropics, can be used to provide that almost imperceptible movement of air that gives a room the feeling of pleasant freshness.

Complaints that a room is stuffy usually mean, not that the air is contaminated in some way, but that it is too warm, or too humid, or that it does not move enough. Cold walls, and especially a cold floor, can cause discomfort if the air is warm.

Doors that are left open frequently cause complaints of draughts. This can be remedied easily by using light doors that are self-closing.

Methods of heating

The method of heating plays an important role in determining comfort. The main problem in designing for thermal comfort is how to distribute heat and air evenly in the space which people are occupying. It is important to avoid heating by single sources of intense heat, and by introducing large gradients in temperature. A difference of 1 to 2°C between the temperatures at floor level and at head height is comfortable; but a difference of 3 to 6°C is unpleasant, particularly if there is a draught along the floor as well. Hot heads and cool feet always make a bad combination! Floor heating avoids this combination: a warm floor with slightly cooler room air is usually thought pleasant; but if the floor temperature rises above about 25°C some people may complain that their feet are too hot.

The choice of method depends on the type of building, the positions of equipment and furniture, and the types of tasks to be carried out in the building, as well as on the costs of installation, fuel, and maintenance. Most forms of heating and ventilation have their limitations as regards comfort, and the designer must be aware of these limitations if the requirements of economy, efficiency, and satisfactory working conditions are to be reconciled. The most troublesome problems arise when the equipment located in a room or building itself makes a comfortable climatic environment difficult to create.

Systems for heating buildings are based on radiation, the circulation of warmed air, or a combination of the two.

Radiators and convectors

The familiar hot-water radiator in fact transmits more heat by convection than by radiation. Sited beneath a window, it reduces downdraught, and helps to compensate for heat loss through the window. Radiation systems give a fairly even distribution of heat. Radiant wall panels are similar to ordinary radiators in performance, but they emit a larger proportion of radiant heat. It is therefore important that they should not be obstructed by furniture or equipment. If they are placed at head height they can cause discomfort to people near them.

Floor, skirting, and ceiling heating
Floor heating normally supplies heat through the whole surface of the floor, which should therefore be relatively unobstructed. It is unsuitable for many industrial buildings but is a satisfactory method of heating offices, provided that the floor temperature is kept below 25°C.

Skirting heating may be either radiant or convective. It can give a comfortable distribution of heat over a space of moderate size, and can check draughts.

Radiant ceiling heating is well suited to warming the whole of a room and its occupants, but care must be taken in designing such a system to ensure that the surface temperature of the panels, and their size, is related to their height above the occupants; if it is not, 'hot head and cold feet' discomfort may arise. Unit heaters located overhead similarly leave the floor space free; they may be radiant heaters or they may blow warm air. As with ceiling panels, the height of the unit heater, its temperature, and its direction have to be planned with care to avoid local centres of discomfort.

Efficient emitters of radiant heat, like an electric fire with its highly polished metal reflector, are extremely useful in directing heat to where it is most needed. Mounted overhead in situations where air heating would be prohibitively expensive, for example in open sheds or where doors are opened frequently, or even out of doors, they provide a simple and economical method of helping to keep people warm, provided they do not cause discomfort by the over-concentration of heat.

Warm-air heating systems
These range from fan-driven convectors, including the unit heaters mentioned above, to complete air conditioning. When room air is recirculated through a heater cabinet, open windows can upset the heat distribution, causing draughts and discomfort. Even when the outlets and inlets are near the floor, this form of heating tends to set up a steep rise in temperature between floor and ceiling. In well-designed air-conditioning systems there is usually sufficient control to maintain freshness without draughts; these systems are now in wider use than even a short time ago: in the past they were rarely installed except in buildings fitted with double glazing and where temperature and humidity had to be closely controlled.

Heat balance

A common method for assessing human response to the thermal environment is to use a heat balance equation. By quantifying heat produced metabolically by the human body, and heat transfer by conduction, convection, radiation, and evaporation in a given environment, the conditions for thermal balance (for example, to maintain a constant body core temperature of 37°C) can be investigated. The required evaporation rate for heat balance represents the thermal strain on the body in hot environments, and the required clothing insulation for heat balance is a useful index when considering cold environments. Heat balance equations can also be used to calculate exposure times beyond which people would be exposed to unacceptable conditions for comfort and health.

Planning for comfort

Plans for comfortable thermal conditions in a new building should begin at a very early stage in its design. Designing comfort in at the outset is much cheaper and more satisfactory than trying to make do after the design has been fixed (Fig 7.5).

Figure 7.5 This is a bank; as with many modern buildings, glass is widely used, and here forms 95% of the wall area. This brings advantages, but also problems such as the fluctuating solar heat load which makes it difficult to provide a satisfactory thermal environment. In this instance, the air conditioning was inadequate, and, to overcome the heat stress on warm, sunny days, cooling panels were added to the ceiling, with a refrigeration plant large enough for an ice-skating rink. To plan a building without considering all aspects of ergonomics as well as aesthetics can prove very embarrassing and very costly.

It is difficult and very costly to install hot-air ducting or underfloor heating when construction has finished; it is easier and cheaper to make the installation part of the original design. At this stage the ergonomist, the heating and ventilation specialist, and the architect can together plan to meet the predicted requirements.

In addition to considering the right conditions to suit the level of activity of people in various parts of the building, the ergonomist advises on the positioning of furniture and equipment, and on other environmental factors such as lighting and the control of noise and vibration.

Heating and ventilation specialists decide on the best method of obtaining the required conditions at the least cost. They know the value of thermal insulations in making it easier to ensure an even temperature, and in reducing fuel costs by minimising heat losses, and they can plan systems with sufficient reserves to provide a comfortable thermal environment in even the coldest winter weather.

Looking at the new building from their own particular angles, these specialists may each spot flaws in the design that have escaped others. For example, too large an area of glass lets in not only light but also, in summer, an unwelcome amount of radiant heat from the sun; in winter it becomes a major site for heat loss, and a troublesome source of draughts. For the design to be satisfactory the specialists need to know much more than merely the size of the building and its rooms. They need to know the number of people who will occupy the building, and the tasks that will be carried out in it; whether heat will be released from equipment, and even whether special provision needs to be made to extract dust or fumes.

Frequently, the problem in planning for comfort is to make the best of a bad job in an existing building. Recognising that bad conditions exist is half the battle. Particularly in places of work and in public buildings, temperatures and humidities should be checked regularly, and reports should be made of the opinions and complaints of the people occupying the building.

Once a problem has been identified, the next step is to make a detailed survey of the area and assess all the factors involved. A good example is a study that was made of the thermal environment in non-ferrous metal foundries. Workers in these foundries complained of excessively hot conditions, and so a team, comprising engineers and ergonomists, investigated the problem. Their work led to modifications in the design of the furnaces, and, as a result, the working conditions were greatly improved, and a considerable economy was achieved through greater fuel efficiency. A less rigorous study might have recommended the provision of fans or some other method of cooling the air; this might have helped the workers but would not have been as efficient overall as the chosen solution, because the main reason for the problem—the design of the furnaces—would not have been identified. The superficial solution would have imposed extra fuel costs rather than reducing them.

An investigation by the physiological unit of the Post Office into the effect of thermal conditions on workers in a single-storey factory showed that glass roofs with inadequate ventilation imposed a most serious heat stress on workers. As a result of the study, roof shading was used to reduce the heat radiation transmitted by the glass, and to lower the temperature of the roof. Powered extractors were installed to create additional ventilation in the roof ridges, and the system of air movement was modified. These simple measures were effective in making the thermal environment more acceptable.

Coping with extremes of temperature

Sometimes it is impossible to provide thermal comfort in a room or building, either because it would be too costly or because a high or low temperature is essential for particular functions to be carried out. An example of the latter is provided by refrigeration cabinets for the bulk storage of food. The aim then is to insulate the individual from the extremes of temperature, and/or to limit the amount of exposure to the extreme environment. In general, it is much easier to deal with cold environments than hot ones. Indeed, often all that is needed is properly designed clothing to insulate the body and to prevent its metabolic heat being lost too quickly (Fig 7.6).It is particularly important to insulate the hands and feet efficiently and to protect them from injury due to contact with materials maintained at very low temperatures, but without impairing mobility and manual dexterity. Protective clothing worn by people in cold-storage rooms is a good example of this.

Coping with very hot conditions is much more difficult, with the additional hazard of clothing catching fire. For furnace workers, to take one example, special clothing has been developed to protect the individual from flames and extreme heat (Fig 7.7).

In some industries people have to enter a hot space to inspect equipment, or for short periods of work. Provided the air is dry and still, people can survive without injury short exposures to very high temperatures: for example, 20 minutes at a temperature of 130°C. As a general rule, however, people should not enter areas with temperatures much exceeding 54°C, unless specially protected and trained, as there is a risk of burns from

Figure 7.6 The protective clothing worn during car engine tests under low-temperature conditions in the cold chamber of the Motor Industry Research Association.

Figure 7.7 This photograph was taken during field trials of a special hot-entry assembly designed to protect furnace workers under hot conditions. After working for approximately 45 minutes in temperatures of up to 200°C, the two men showed no fatigue and no sweat loss.

contact with highly heat-conductive materials such as metals.

Recently, the development of special equipment has largely removed the need for people to endure unaided the discomfort and danger of very hot environments. A suit has been developed through which cool air is fed to all parts of the body by means of an air line. Breathing apparatus, which may be needed in the presence of noxious fumes, is also available.

Humidity and air movement become very important at high temperatures because they affect the amount of sweat which can be evaporated from the body surface. Even young, fit men who are acclimatised to heat cannot work hard for long if the wet-bulb temperature (related to humidity) exceeds about 32°C. Enough heat cannot be lost from the body surface, and body temperature therefore rises. Individuals differ widely in their ability to tolerate increases in body temperature, but when it rises above 38.5°C, heat exhaustion and collapse become serious problems. Someone with experience will know when to leave a hot environment and cool down, but heat collapse can develop suddenly, and the inexperienced may be caught unawares. If someone is overcome by the heat it is vital to get them into cool conditions as quickly as possible, and, provided there is no delay, recovery is usually rapid and complete. Tasks in such environments should, therefore, never be left to a single person; it requires a group of three or more, and each of them should have frequent and rigidly controlled breaks in cool conditions. The Factories Act lays down certain provisions which are not only statutory obligations but also very sensible guidelines to follow.

Further reading

American Society of Heating, Refrigerating and Air-conditioning Engineers (1965/66). *ASHRAE guide and data book*, Part 1: Fundamentals and equipment; Part 2: Applications. New York: ASHRAE

BROUHA, L. (1967). *Physiology in industry*, 2nd edn. Oxford: Pergamon Press

BURTON, A.C. and EDHOLM, O.G. (1955). *Man in a cold environment*. London: Edward Arnold

CHRENKO, F.A. (ed) (1974). *Bedford's basic principles of ventilation and heating*, 3rd edn. London: H.K. Lewis

CLARKE, R.P. and EDHOLM, O.G. (1985). *Man and his thermal environment*. London: Edward Arnold

EDHOLM, O.G. (1967). *The biology of work*. London: Weidenfeld and Nicholson

ELLIS, F.P., SMITH, F.E., and WALTERS, J.D. (1972). *Br. J. Ind. Med.*, **29**, 361. 'Measurement of environmental warmth in SI units'

FANGER, P.O. (1970). *Thermal comfort: analysis and applications in environmental engineering*. Copenhagen: Danish Technical Press

INSTITUTION OF HEATING AND VENTILATING ENGINEERS (1965). *A guide to current practice*. London: IHVE

INTERNATIONAL STANDARDS ORGANISATION (1981). *Hot environments—estimation of the heat stress on working man, based on the WBGT index*, ISO 7243. London: ISO

MCINTYRE, D.A. (1980). *Indoor climate*. London: Applied Science Publishers

Chapter 8

The environment—noise and vibration

In this chapter, sound and its measurement are explained. Also the effects of noise on health, communication, annoyance, and efficiency are discussed, along with ways of controlling them. The chapter concludes with a discussion of the effects of vibration on people.

What noise does

Noise is a problem for three main reasons: people do not like it, it damages their hearing, and it has a bad effect on working efficiency. These three effects are not necessarily related to one another. For instance, a noise which is very annoying may not be loud enough to damage hearing, or make people work less well. On the other hand, there is the rather alarming possibility that noises that do not annoy some individuals may damage their hearing or impair their efficiency. It is important, therefore, to distinguish the various effects from one another and not to assume that all is well just because people in a noisy environment seem to be contented. Equally, of course, a barrage of complaints about noise may tell one very little about the sounds that people are experiencing, but perhaps rather more about the general level of morale. It is important, therefore, to have some idea of the effects which noise may have on people.

Sound and its measurement

What we perceive as sound are rapid oscillations in air pressure at the ear (Fig 8.1). The actual pressure amplitudes are extremely small; however, the effects on people can be serious. Sound perception depends on the pressure amplitude and the rapidity of the oscillations, and two technical terms are used to describe these, as follows.

The first term is the decibel (dB), which is used as a measure of the pressure amplitude. We perceive this pressure as loudness. The difference in pressure between the loudest and the quietest sounds is immense (about 10 million to 1), and normal pressure units would be cumbersome in practice. The decibel scale (a logarithmic scale) simplifies the situation (giving a corresponding range of 0 to about 140); we can thus manageably use the same units for all practical situations. This simplification is shown in Fig 8.2, which also gives an indication of the decibel level of typical sounds.

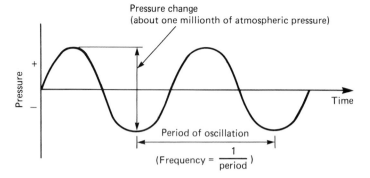

Figure 8.1 A time graph of the air pressure fluctuation at the ear which would be perceived as a pure tone.

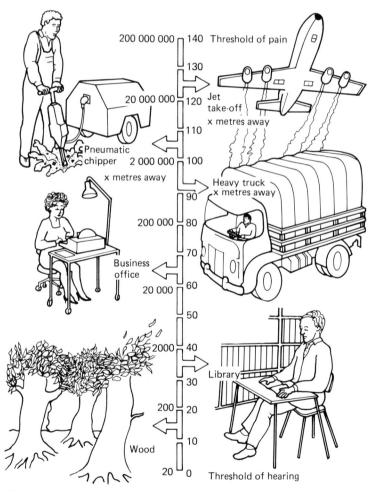

Figure 8.2 Actual sound pressure in micropascals, and pressure expressed in decibels, for typical sounds.

It is necessary to remember that the decibel relates to the logarithm of the ratio of the sound pressure to a pressure of 20 micropascals, which is approximately our hearing threshold (the faintest sound that one can hear). A doubling of pressure is equivalent to a 6 dB change and a tenfold increase to a 20 dB change. Thus the sound pressure of a 106 dB noise is twice that of a 100 dB noise—an increase of 100%, not 6%. In human terms, however, the decibel is a convenient unit in that the smallest change that the ear can detect is roughly one or two dB.

The second term is frequency, which we perceive as pitch. The frequency in hertz (Hz) of a sound is the number of pressure oscillations per second; high-pitched sounds are of high frequency, and low-pitched sounds of low frequency. Although a few actual sounds contain only one frequency of pressure oscillation, most noises are much more complex. Fortunately, we can regard such sounds as a combination of a number of simple sounds, each with a different frequency and sound pressure. Instruments are available to do this 'frequency analysis' of noise.

Our sensitivity to sound depends on the frequency. Our ears are most sensitive at about 3000 Hz, and our sensation is limited to a range from about 20 to about 20 000 Hz (Fig 8.3). Most noise-measuring instruments have the facility to take into account this variation with frequency of the sensitivity of the human ear. The method in common use is called an 'A-weighting', and the corresponding unit of pressure is dB(A).

A variety of equipment is available to measure noise. The simplest, giving little more than the dB(A) value, need not be over expensive and can often tell roughly how good or bad a situation is. More expensive equipment can take noise variation into account, give information on

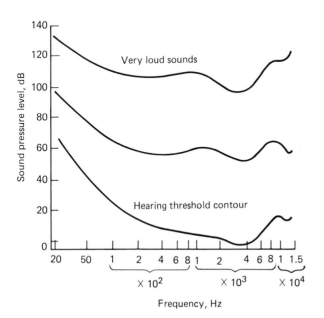

Figure 8.3 The frequency-dependent sensitivity of the human ear: each line is a 'contour' of equal loudness (as judged subjectively by listeners).

frequency content, and so on. The important thing is that the user has instruction on how to ensure that the measurements taken are valid.

Detrimental effects of noise

Effects on the ear

Most people realise that a noise can harm their hearing if it is sufficiently loud, but they usually think in terms of some quite exceptionally violent sound, producing an effect as dramatic as the rupture of an eardrum. In fact, deafness can be produced in a much more insidious way by continual exposure to noise which might well be regarded as acceptable in ordinary life. The deafness in this case is not due to any effect on the eardrum but results from damage to the delicate mechanism which converts the sound energy into impulses travelling through the nerves to the brain.

We all know that our hearing tends to get worse as we grow older. This hearing loss is usually a reduction in sensitivity to higher frequency sounds. Initially, only very high frequencies are affected, and this may not be noticed. However, the loss of sensation is likely to spread to lower frequencies until perception of consonant speech sounds is affected, so that the person thinks simply that others are not speaking clearly—not realising that he or she is going deaf.

The person suffering from hearing loss arising from exposure to excessive noise experiences a similar insidious pattern of irreversible change. However, it happens earlier and may be more marked. The hearing loss associated with excessive exposure to noise is often such that low-pitched sounds are not impaired, so that 'turning up the volume' to improve perception of high-pitched sounds leads to excessive loudness in the low-pitched sounds. To make matters worse, the individual may also suffer from tinnitus (permanent ringing in the ears).

Hearing loss is measured by means of 'audiometry', where the perception threshold (the smallest sound pressure that can be detected) is measured at a number of frequencies. Fortunately, an audiometric test can detect hearing loss long before the person recognises any loss. Exposure to excessive noise usually leads to a marked reduction in hearing at about 4000 Hz (Fig 8.4). It should be emphasised that the normal loss in hearing with age can be expected to continue, even if an individual leaves a noisy job because of suspected hearing damage, so that the deafness may eventually become severe. Audiometry needs to be used for early detection and also to identify individuals who are particularly susceptible to noise-induced hearing loss.

It is usually accepted that if the amount of a noise varies over time, then its effect can be integrated over a period of time to give a 'noise dose'. The variation between individuals in susceptibility to noise-induced hearing loss is high, and one cannot identify a sharp borderline beyond which hearing loss will or will not occur. However, most national specifications consider a level of 85 to 90 dB(A) as a criterion for action against noise.

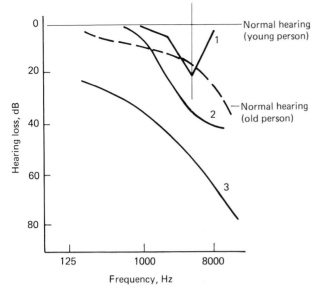

Figure 8.4 The various stages of occupational hearing loss: Stage 1, first detected on audiogram; Stage 3, detectable by the patient.

Effects on communication

Noise has a masking effect whereby it makes sounds that we want to hear difficult or impossible to detect or understand. Thus, excessive noise may mask the sound of warning signals and other auditory information, and the systems designer must take this into account.

Speech communication can deteriorate significantly in noise. Signal to noise ratio (the difference in the levels of speech sounds and noise) is obviously an important factor, but matters can be improved if the speech and the noise have a different character or have some 'binaural' element. Thus, if the noise itself consists of speech sounds, communication is very poor, whilst if we can arrange matters so that the noise is in both ears and the speech only in one, communication may be improved. Much depends on the message itself. By reducing vocabulary size, avoiding easily confused words, embedding critical words in special phrases, giving feedback, and using other message design methods, one can improve communication in noise.

One can estimate the possible effects of a noise on communication by measuring it and taking its frequency characteristics into account. The dB(A) value gives some indication, but more sophisticated techniques (eg the 'Articulation Index') are available.

Annoying effects

The annoyance of a noise is very much dependent on the information that the noise brings with it. However, on the whole, the louder the noise is, the more people complain about it. Even quite faint sounds, however, may annoy some people, and there are large differences between individuals in the kinds of noise which they find most objectionable. This makes it impossible to lay down firm rules about this aspect of noise but, other things being equal, most people find high-pitched noises more annoying than low-pitched ones, and interrupted or sudden, unexpected noises more annoying than steady, prolonged ones. Sounds whose sources are unknown are also especially irritating, and people often complain much more about a noise when they feel that it is unnecessary and a result of thoughtlessness. This means that explanations and apologies may sometimes do more than anything else to reduce the annoyance caused by a noise.

Effects on work

Some laboratory experiments have shown that noise lowers the efficiency of working, while other experiments have failed to do so. This is probably not a contradiction, but merely means that some types of task are easily affected while others are not. If, for example, a button has to be pressed when a light comes on, and one knows when this is likely to happen, one can probably do it just as well under noisy conditions as in quiet ones. Furthermore, if you happen to be feeling rather sleepy, and nothing very much happens in the task to keep you awake, the noise may actually prevent drowsiness and so make your reactions faster. The bad effects of noise come rather when work is done under fairly stimulating conditions— if, for example, one has to pay attention to a lot of information at once, so that it is impossible to relax for a second.

There is still a lot of argument about the types of task affected by noise, how they are affected, and whether laboratory results can be applied to actual situations. However, the influence of noise may be critical in tasks where the cost of mistakes (in terms of product loss or safety) is important.

An important point to remember is that the effects of noise which have been proved have only appeared when the noise was very loud: in most of the cases which have shown positive results, the sound pressure level of the noise has been greater than about 90 dB(A). This level is roughly the level which has to be regarded as a threat to hearing; and, therefore, if precautions are taken to prevent deafness, they will also tend to prevent effects on working efficiency. Nevertheless, it should be remembered that short spells of work under noisy conditions may reduce the efficiency of work even though they may not lead to permanent deafness.

However, we also need to remember that the reduced communication and annoyance arising from noise can also lead to reduced performance, either directly or via increased absenteeism from work.

What to do about noise

We are concerned here primarily with hearing loss. Clearly, environmental noise pollution is of great concern, but it is considered to be beyond the scope of this chapter. What about the noisy situation where hearing loss is not a problem? It would be necessary to take cognisance of all complaints of noise as possible indicators of other problems, and also to anticipate that noisy new equipment may lead to new problems. It must also be accepted that noise may affect performance. However, much depends on the situation and the expectations that go with it. Very rough rules of thumb can be used (eg try to keep general office noise levels below about 50 dB(A), or, say, 55 dB(A) if the increased noise level would help by masking some speech sounds within the office and thus increasing personal privacy), but these should be subservient to an assessment of the full human situation.

If hearing loss is of concern, clearly the first thing to do is to measure the noise. Even if there are no complaints, it is probably wise to measure the noise if it seems loud enough to make ordinary speech difficult—the level may be sufficiently high to be affecting the hearing of some people, even though they do not recognise it. A simple sound level meter giving dB(A), as illustrated in Fig 8.5, may be sufficient initially, although a dosimeter attached to an individual, as illustrated in Fig 8.6, may be necessary if he or she is exposed to varying noise levels because he or she moves about or the process varies. Such measurements will indicate if further action is necessary, and the cost of the instrument need not be high. The important thing is that the user have sufficient training to ensure that the measurements are valid. A noise level map such as that illustrated in Fig 8.7 will give more useful planning information than simple spot checks.

Figure 8.5 A typical sound level meter in use. (Courtesy Brüel and Kjaer Ltd)

Figure 8.6 Measuring noise dose over time with a dosimeter. (Courtesy Brüel and Kjaer Ltd)

Before much can be done about treating a known noisy situation, information is needed on the frequency characteristics and perhaps time variation characteristics of the noise. This will demand more expensive equipment and most probably the services of an experienced noise consultant.

The consultative proposals for the protection of hearing at work prepared as part of the Health and Safety at Work legislation in the UK provide useful guidance on what to do if noise levels are high. A hearing conservation programme should include consideration of education, audiometric screening, the treatment of noisy areas, and hearing protection.

If the level of noise is too high, the best cure is to stop it at source, by paying attention to silencing, maintenance, and the mounting of vibrating machinery on isolating mounts to stop transmission of the sound away from the machine. When all this has been done, however, there are bound to be some sources of noise which are still too loud. Where possible they should be kept away from people—insulating walls should be put in between the noise and the person. Where this cannot be done, it may be worth while to increase the amount of soft absorbent surfaces in the room. Many interiors have hard walls, floors, and ceilings, which reflect the noise back and forth, making it unnecessarily loud. With the common types of absorbent materials this treatment can only reduce the noise to a limited extent. The

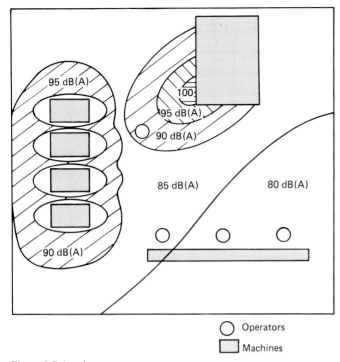

○ Operators

▨ Machines

Figure 8.7 A noise map.

reduction may be worthwhile if the noise is near the critical level, but treatment at source is preferable. Noise treatment is not an area for the amateur, and it is probably best to call in a noise treatment specialist at an early stage. Probably the most economic measure is to identify noisy equipment before purchase, and consider noise at an early stage of planning.

Nevertheless, there may remain intractable cases where the noise is still too high. The only answer then is for people to use individual ear protectors. The most widely known of these are earplugs, and if properly fitted these can do a great deal of good. They are certainly a great improvement over the use of cotton wool, which is not very effective in reducing the amount of noise reaching the ear and may give a false sense of security. Another way of protecting the ears is to wear muffs, like a pair of headphones but without the phones themselves. Whichever kind of ear defender is used, the most that can be expected is that they will reduce the noise by some 30 to 40 dB, and this will be at high frequencies. There is, therefore, a limit to the amount of noise to which people should be exposed, even with hearing protectors. It is vital that any form of hearing protection used should fit well, as noise will get through the smallest gap. It is also important that protectors are worn at all times, as periods without protectors have an inordinately large effect on hearing. What is sometimes forgotten is that the user may not notice a steady deterioration in efficiency of a protector, and it is important that hearing protectors are regularly inspected and well maintained.

If the noise is high enough to warrant protection then each person should have his or her hearing tested when first experiencing these conditions, and at intervals from then onwards. The reason for this is that some people are much more susceptible to hearing damage than others, while a few will manage to work in noise above the critical level without becoming deaf. Unfortunately, there is no way of predicting which individuals will fall into either group, and, therefore, deterioration should be identified as soon as it begins to appear, even if the individual has not noticed it.

The biggest problem is how to make sure that people who may be exposed to noise realise the dangers and take the necessary trouble to protect themselves. Some people, who do not mind noise, tend to assert that it is quite harmless and to neglect commonsense precautions. The effects of noise above a certain level are real, and every precaution should be taken not only to minimise the risk of permanent hearing damage but also to prevent needless inefficiency and annoyance.

Vibration and people

The effects of hand vibration on health, and whole body vibration on comfort, health, and performance, are discussed here, together with ways of dealing with them.

Vibrating surfaces give rise to sound. However, people are often in direct contact with vibrating objects themselves, and this may be of concern. During most forms of transport you are shaken about to some extent. In some jobs, for example the pilot of a helicopter, the vibration can be very strong. Many people also work with powered equipment so that their hands only are exposed to vibration, for example those working with road drills or chipping hammers. These two general types of exposure give rise to different effects, and it is usual to separate them into 'hand–arm vibration' and 'whole-body vibration'.

Hand–arm vibration

Occurrence
If one works with a chipping hammer, a pedestal grinder, a chain saw, or any of a number of other processes, the hands have to control the tool or the material being processed, and as a result are exposed to a lot of vibration, often coupled with a need to exert quite considerable forces. This may lead to a phenomenon known as 'Vibration White Finger' (or VWF).

Vibration White Finger
Some people (mostly females) suffer from a condition known as Raynaud's disease, where the fingers may go white, cold, and insensitive in certain situations. VWF is similar but arises as a result of excessive exposure to hand–arm vibration. Initially the problem is simply of intermittent tingling, numbness, or blanching of the fingertips. However, left unattended, it may develop to an extent where the fingers lose their dexterity and are even physically damaged. Initially, the attacks of VWF tend to occur only when

the individual is cold or wet. As a consequence, attacks may not occur when the person is actually being exposed to vibration, and the average person may not realise that there is a connection between the vibration and the attacks.

What to do about VWF
Perhaps the most important thing is for more people to recognise that vibrating tools may lead to health problems, and then to look out for VWF. Once recognised, a combination of vibration damping of the hand tool, the use of warm, dry gloves in cold, damp conditions, and schedules designed to keep daily exposure time low can hold VWF at bay or even eradicate it.

Whole-body vibration

Discomfort
Most of us would say that it is uncomfortable to be bounced about in the back of a truck driving across a bumpy field. However, it may be a bit of a thrill, and some even pay for such pleasures at a funfair. Essentially, the degree of discomfort that one would put to a certain vibration will relate to one's expectation of that situation, the task that one wishes to perform, and a number of other factors.

However, vibration discomfort or 'ride' may nevertheless be an important factor when a customer makes a choice between competing forms of transport. Also discomfort due to whole-body vibration may influence performance. Given two similar situations, there are data available to help the designer decide whether one vibration condition is more or less uncomfortable than another.

Performance
Whole-body vibration may affect task performance directly by making a visual display difficult to see, by making it difficult for hand or foot controls to be operated accurately, and possibly indirectly by affecting our cognitive processes. There is little evidence for the indirect effects, but the direct effects are a well-recognised problem in many critical situations—for example, the fighter pilot during the buffeting of low-altitude flying.

Although they have been investigated extensively, consideration of the direct effects on vision and control performance presents complex issues beyond the scope of this chapter. There is a great deal of information for designers, but tasks are so different that resort to simulation and mockups is usually a part of the design process.

Health
There is still argument as to whether whole-body vibration does or does not affect health. This is mostly as a result of the difficulties and cost of mounting good epidemiological investigations of the health of people exposed to whole-body vibration. The health problems that might be expected are the increased and earlier onset of back problems, and (possibly) digestive and cardiovascular disorders. In view of the doubts, the designer must ensure that vibration levels are not excessive and that people are not forced into unusual postures.

What to do about whole-body vibration

We do not have a unique means of perceiving vibration in the same way that the eye and the ear are designed to perceive light and sound. As a result, it is usually difficult to predict the effects of whole-body vibration. However, very often the physical characteristics of the human body and its components have a strong influence, so that vibration in the frequency range from about 3 to 8 Hz has a marked effect on many human responses. In these cases, avoidance of frequencies of this order is a good design rule of thumb. Where vibration is high, seated operators can use anti-vibration seats, which will significantly reduce the vibration experienced (Fig 8.8).

National and international standards are available to give design guidance. However, these should not be used as a rigid set of rules, but must be considered in relation to the specific features of the problem under study.

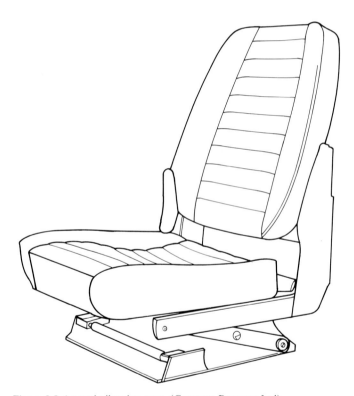

Figure 8.8 An anti-vibration seat. (Courtesy Bostrum Ltd)

Further reading

BURNS, W. (1973). *Noise and man*. London: John Murray

CROOME, D.J. (1977). *Noise, buildings and people*. Oxford: Pergamon

GUIGNARD, J.C. and KING, P.F. (1972). *Aeromedical aspects of vibration and noise*, AGARDograph No. 151. AGARD

KRYTER, K.D. (1970). *The effects of noise on man*. London: Academic Press

MOORE, B.C.J. (1982). *Introduction to the psychology of hearing*. London: Academic Press

TAYLOR, W. and PELMEAR, P.L. (1975). *Vibration white finger in industry*. London: Academic Press

VAN COTT, H.P. and KINKADE R.G. (eds) (1972). *Human engineering guide to equipment design*. Washington: US Government Printing Office

(1978) *Audiometry in industry*, Discussion Document. London: HMSO

WORLD HEALTH ORGANISATION (1980). *Environmental health criteria, 12: Noise*. Geneva: WHO

BRUEL & KJAER (1982). *Noise control: principles and practice*. Hounslow, Mddx: Bruel & Kjaer (UK) Ltd.

(1981) *Protection of hearing at work*, HSE Consultative Document. London: HMSO

(1981) *Some aspects of noise and hearing loss*, Background to the HSC consultative document on the protection of hearing at work. London: HMSO

Chapter 9

The environment—vision and lighting

The first part of this chapter deals with the principles of good lighting; these are common to both daylight and artificial light, and the two are not distinguished. In the second part, which deals with practical design considerations, the essential features of each type of source are examined independently. The general requirements for good lighting are summarised in the final section.

Good lighting is necessary if work is to be done well and in comfort. It must help people to see the details of their work with the greatest possible speed and clarity, it must provide safe and congenial working conditions, and it must be easy to maintain and inexpensive to run. Lighting can be made to suit the task, but unless it also suits the wider area around the task and the people occupying that area, it will be judged unsatisfactory.

The principles of good lighting

The amount of light necessary for good task performance depends on the nature of the task, the sharpness of the task performer's vision, and the environment in which the task is carried out. The minimum amount of light required for reading, writing, and many manual tasks is about 10 lux. At one time this was all the light by which most people had to read, write, and sew after dark; but people can only work slowly and with difficulty under such conditions, and need about 30 times as much light to carry out their tasks easily and efficiently.

The Chartered Institution of Building Services in Great Britain publishes a Code of Recommendations for Lighting Building Interiors, which classifies a wide range of different visual tasks in terms of the levels of illumination accepted as good practice. Some examples of the CIBS Code are given in Table 9.1. It is possible to measure the existing level of illumination in any place, easily and cheaply, by using a light meter, and then to compare this value with the CIBS standard recommended for the type of task.

In the design of good lighting, safety and welfare should be taken into account as well as visual efficiency. In some tasks where the visual demands are small, it is usual to recommend levels of illumination based on standards of safety, welfare, and amenity, and so, by creating a pleasing environment, to interest people in their surroundings and give them a

Table 9.1 Examples showing amounts of light required for adequate visual performance (from the CIBS Code, 1984)

Visual task	Recommended Illumination (lux)
Assembly and inspection tasks	
rough work	300
medium work	500
fine work	750
very fine work	1000
Weaving tasks	
jute and hemp	300
fine woollens	750
inspection	1500
Sheet metal work	500
Plastics moulding and sheet fabrication	300
Woodworking	
rough sawing	300
planing, medium bench and machine work	500
fine bench and machine work, finishing	750

sense of wellbeing and a will to perform tasks well. The minimum 'amenity' level is 200 lux.

Lighting the work and the surroundings

At any working place, the person can see the task itself, the immediate background to the task, and the general surroundings (walls, ceiling, floor, and objects in the room). The eyes tend to be attracted to the brighter and more colourful parts of the field of view, and so light and colour should be used to make the task or working area the focus of attention. Light may be directed on to the work, or special local lighting may be provided to match the needs of the task and also the general level of lighting. The level of brightness required for any task is determined partly by the degree of detail the person has to observe and the time allowed for this, partly by the reflection characteristics of the task itself, and partly by the general level of brightness in the room. In practice it is advisable to plan the illumination first in relation to what is required for the task itself, and then to plan the brightness of the other parts of the room—to give proper emphasis, visual comfort, and interest.

Freedom from glare

Glare may cause discomfort or reduce the ability to see, or both. It occurs when some parts of the field of view are excessively bright in relation to the general level of brightness.

The degree of glare resulting directly from light sources depends on such factors as the brightness and area of the sources, their position in the person's field of view, and the average brightness of the surroundings against which they are seen. Glare often causes discomfort without affecting the ability to see the task, particularly in very bright surroundings. It is possible to avoid this discomfort by reducing the contrast between the sources of light, whether daylight or artificial light, and their surroundings. The brightness and area of visible sources of light should be limited and graded into the brightness of their surroundings. Similarly, there should be no sharp line between the work and the surroundings; a gradual change in brightness and colour is desirable. Moderately light working surfaces are preferable to very dark, highly coloured or polished surfaces. The reflection of light sources in polished or glossy surfaces may cause glare. Light reflected on a polished surface of a piece of equipment (Figs 9.1, 9.2, and 9.3) may not only distract the operator but may make it impossible to see clearly such essential details as graduations on a scale. Often the only solution is to replace polished surfaces by matt ones; but the effect can be reduced by changing the position of the light sources, so that reflections in polished surfaces fall outside the normal field of view. Alternatively, the brightness of the source can be lowered, or light rather than dark surfaces can be used in the immediate background to the task.

With increasing levels of illumination, the problem of glare discomfort becomes more severe. The CIBS Code provides a means of controlling

Figure 9.1 Reflected glare on the polished surface of a marking-off table reduces visibility.

Figure 9.2 This planing machine is in a place well lit by conventional standards, but there is a bright reflection off the proper line of vision, which distracts the attention away from the cutters.

Figure 9.3 Re-lighting placed the reflection of a lower-brightness fitting on the cutters themselves, attracting the attention to where it should be.

glare by limiting the permissible level of glare in terms of a Glare Index. This is a numerical value derived from the type of light fitting, its brightness and position, the size of the room, and the reflectances of its surfaces. These recommended values are tolerance limits of glare discomfort based on good lighting practice, and are related to the conditions of different occupations. The Code publishes recommended limiting Glare Indices appropriate to particular environments and visual tasks. Glare Index Limits vary between 16 and 28. The values of limiting Glare Index do not correlate, however, with the recommended levels of illumination. Table 9.2 gives the limiting Glare Indices for the industrial tasks listed in Table 9.1, and it will be seen that, in general, the greater the difficulty of the visual task the higher is the level of illumination and the lower the Glare Index.

Table 9.2 Some examples of limiting Glare Index (from the CIBS Code, 1984)

Visual task	Limiting Glare Index
Assembling and inspection	
rough work	25
medium work	22
fine work	19
very fine work	—
Weaving	
jute and hemp	15
fine woollens	19
inspection	—
Sheet metal work	22
Plastics moulding and sheet fabrication	25
Woodworking	
rough sawing	22
planing, medium bench and machine work	22
fine bench and machine work, finishing	22

Compliance with the Glare Index system does not call for changes in good current practice, but should eliminate some of the worst examples which occur at present.

Freedom from flicker

Discharge lamps (sodium discharge, mercury discharge, or tubular fluorescent) operating on alternating current produce light which varies in each cycle. The flicker is not normally seen when lamps operate on a 50 Hz supply, since it occurs at twice the frequency of the supply, but under such conditions a person may get the impression that rotating machinery or other moving objects have slowed down or are stationary. The stroboscopic effect can be minimised by operating adjacent lamps in a fitting on special circuits so that they flicker on and off alternately, or by connecting adjacent lamps in a room to different phases of a three-phase supply. Flicker is more likely to be troublesome at high levels of illumination, and special care should be taken in the design of such installations. Flicker may be apparent at the extreme ends of fluorescent tubes where the fluctuation in the light emitted occurs at mains frequency, but this can be overcome by screening the ends of the tubes from direct view. Some people are much more sensitive to flicker than others, and complaints of flicker should be treated with care and consideration.

Shadows and modelling

It is possible either to sharpen or to soften the form and surface texture of an object by changing the direction of the light falling on it. This effect is generally known as modelling, and it can be used to improve the visibility of the details of some tasks, particularly in industrial inspection processes. Where it is necessary, the modelling light should be provided in addition to the general lighting in the room, and the light sources should be specially located in relation to the task (Figs 9.4 and 9.5).

Colour and illumination

The appearance of coloured surfaces depends on the amount of light reflected from them, and on the type of lighting used. Most types of artificial light sources distort the appearance of colours seen under them, as compared with their appearance in daylight. For many inspection tasks requiring judgement or recognition of colour, the artificial lighting should be designed to minimise this distortion. For this type of task, however, owing to the variations in daylight, artificial lighting is often preferred to daylight because it is possible to maintain the same quality and amount of light at all times. Appropriate use of colour can help to maintain attention on the task, improve safety and amenity, and reduce glare from windows and light fittings.

Figure 9.4 The direction from which light reaches the work is important. Reflector fittings mounted above the benches in this joinery shop do not illuminate the side of the work in the vice.

Figure 9.5 A remodelled lighting installation in the same joinery shop gives good distribution of light over all the working surfaces.

Visual rest and relaxation

Prolonged close visual inspection is tiring, and the task performer should be able to relax the eyes occasionally by looking away from the task towards some distant object or surface, for example by looking out of a window even though the view itself may not be particularly interesting. When no windows can be seen, it should be possible to look some distance beyond the immediate work place. It is important, however, that such views should not be so bright that the eyes take time to adjust to the light when the task is resumed.

Posture and fatigue

If the task involves fine detail and the lighting is poor, it is necessary to peer at it, often in a cramped position, and this can result in visual strain and muscular fatigue. With good lighting, it will be possible to see fine detail from a comfortable distance, and so a more natural position can be adopted which can be maintained more comfortably if the work is arranged at or near eye level.

Lighting for movement within a building

Accidents may be caused if people pass from well-lit areas into others which are inadequately lit, because the eyes take some time to become adjusted to changes in illumination. The lighting of all areas should be properly designed to enable people to move safely within a building at all times.

Fig 9.6 demonstrates some of the ways in which lighting can be used to illuminate an object, for example in an inspection process:

- to distinguish an object from its background;
- to reveal its shape;
- to reveal its surface texture;
- to enable any markings on its surface to be easily seen.

These effects can be obtained by careful choice of the direction of the lighting and by illuminating the object and its background by different amounts. It is seen that these functional requirements are, in certain respects, conflicting and may not always be achieved together. It may be necessary to provide more than one lighting arrangement for different parts of the same task, either at different points in the working area or combined in a lighting console and capable of being switched independently by the user.

However, there are many circumstances in which optimum viewing conditions cannot be achieved by lighting from units in fixed positions, and so some form of adjustable unit may be required. The object used in Fig 9.6 is a hollow cylinder of mid-grey colour, with a slight surface texture. Lettering in black and white has been printed on its surface, and the object has been placed against a mid-grey background.

Practical design considerations

Daylight

The windows or skylights in a building can be designed to give the right amount and form of daylight needed for particular tasks. It is important to co-ordinate the design of the interior of the building and the layout of its contents with the design of daylighting systems, so that they do not obstruct the light.

In general, the aim in the design of work daylighting is to distribute light evenly over a large working area. This is only possible if the light comes from skylights rather than from side windows, though the latter are desirable to provide visual relaxation and contact with the outside. Systems where the daylight comes from only one direction, such as a north-light roof, will limit sun penetration. Floor and ceiling surfaces should be light in colour, to reflect the light and to minimise contrast with the glazed areas.

The uniformity ratio (the ratio of the minimum illumination to the average) should not be less than 0.7 when top-lighting is used for daylight admittance (BSI DD73: 1982).

If a higher level of illumination is needed on the task itself, then it is better to provide additional local artificial lighting than to have too high a level of daylighting over the whole working area. The variation which occurs in natural lighting throughout the day and over the year is desirable for human wellbeing; a uniform environment is dull and monotonous. Such changes do not appreciably affect the performance of the visual task, as the eye adjusts itself readily to slow changes in brightness in the task when these are accompanied by comparable changes in the surroundings. Thus, it is customary to express the amount of daylighting in a building not in terms of illumination level but as a ratio, called the daylight factor, which is the fraction of the total light available, from the whole sky, which reaches the point where the task is carried out. The daylight factor is a geometrical property of the building and remains relatively constant irrespective of changes in sky brightness and in the absolute level of illumination.

For most industrial tasks the recommended daylight factor is about 5%. This provides an illumination of at least 250 lux for 85% of the working year from 0800 to 1700 hours GMT. Window orientation and the external level of unobstructed light are important factors in determining the illuminancies achieved by daylight.

Artificial light

Artificial lighting can often be tailored to the needs of the specific tasks in a workplace, bearing in mind future changes in the nature and disposition of the work to be carried out. A general installation of artificial lighting which gives a good distribution of light over the whole interior is usually required during the hours of darkness, supplemented by some additional local lighting where necessary, depending on the task requirements.

The structural details of the inside of a building, such as beams and columns, and the layout of equipment and furniture often influence the

Figure 9.6 Examples of effect of varying illumination of an object.
(a) Direct light from the front: surface markings clearly seen; does little to reveal shape; does not reveal texture or distinguish object from its background.
(b) Diffused light obliquely from two sides: surface markings clearly seen; does little to reveal shape; does not reveal texture; no improvement in ability to distinguish object from background.
(c) Direct light obliquely from two sides: surface markings clearly seen; does not reveal texture; some improvement in revelation of shape and in ability to distinguish object from background.
(d) Direct light obliquely from right side, diffused light obliquely from left: surface markings not easily visible on shadowed side; shape clearly revealed; texture becoming apparent; object clearly distinguished from background.
(e) Direct light perpendicularly from two opposite sides: surface markings not easily visible in shadow at front; some loss of visibility at sides on account of specular reflections; shape clearly revealed; some texture visible on surface; object clearly distinguished from background.
(f) Direct light perpendicularly from right side, diffused light perpendicularly from left: surface markings not easily visible in shadows; some loss of visibility on account of specular reflections; shape clearly revealed; some texture visible on surface; object clearly distinguished from background.

choice of the artificial lighting installation. Comparatively uniform illumination can be obtained only when the pool of light produced by any one fitting overlaps those of adjacent fittings; the size of individual pools of light depends upon the type of fitting and its mounting height. The spacing between fittings must be related to their mounting height, and for each type of fitting there is a spacing/height ratio which gives optimum uniformity of illumination.

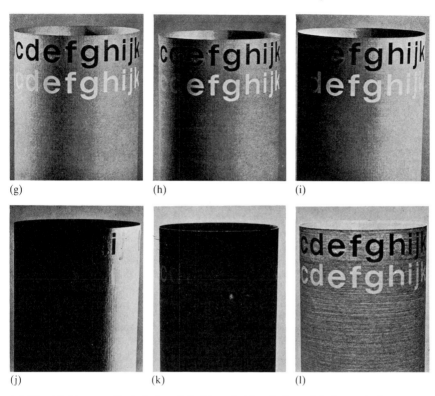

(g)   (h)   (i)

(j)   (k)   (l)

(g) Direct light perpendicularly from left side and obliquely from right front: shadow softened; surface markings revealed; shape apparent; some texture visible on surface; object slightly distinguished from background.

(h) Direct light obliquely from right front and obliquely from left rear: surface markings not easily visible in shadow; shape clearly revealed; some texture visible on surface; object clearly distinguished from background.

(i) Direct light obliquely from right front and perpendicularly from right: surface markings not easily visible in shadow; shape clearly revealed; some texture visible on surface; object clearly distinguished from background.

(j) Direct light obliquely from right rear: object clearly distinguished from background; vertical texture on surface clearly revealed; surface markings practically indistinguishable on account of shadow and specular reflections; shape not readily apparent.

(k) Direct light from above to rear: object clearly distinguished from background; surface markings not visible; texture on surface not visible; shape not readily apparent.

(l) Direct light from above to front: object clearly distinguished from background; surface markings clearly seen; shape readily seen; horizontal texture on surface clearly revealed.

There are many different types of electric light sources, and the choice for a particular situation depends on the level of illumination required and the standard of colour judgement involved in the visual task, as well as on economic factors such as costs, the annual hours of use, lamp life, and ease of maintenance. The installed load per 100 lux using the most popular industrial light sources (tubular fluorescent lamps or high pressure sodium discharge lamps) is 4 W/m^2 (watts per square metre) and 3 W/m^2, respectively. The main types of electric lamps suitable for industrial use are described in the appendix to this chapter.

Supplementing daylight with artificial light

Artificial light is commonly used in buildings during daytime to provide additional local lighting on the task, or to produce special effects such as modelling, silhouette, and specular reflections, or to illuminate surfaces inaccessible to the daylighting. However, there are many instances where the daylight is inadequate or is obstructed within the building, and it may be necessary to consider the use of artificial light as a permanent supplement to daylight. There are three points to consider, as follows.

• The artificial lighting must be planned for continuous integration with the daylight, and not for use solely after dark.

• The amount of supplementary light should raise the level of illumination at least to that necessary for the visual tasks involved, and areas so lit should compare favourably with areas receiving maximum daylight.

• The colour of the supplementary light should be of a sufficiently good match to daylight to prevent any noticeable difference in the colour of the two sources or in their colour rendering.

Good integration of artificial light with daylight can increase the use of available floor space by eliminating dark areas and minimising shadows, especially in work areas with north-light types of roof. In side-lit rooms it enables more efficient use to be made of the areas remote from the windows, and reduces glare through the windows themselves.

It is important that these ideas are not carried to the illogical conclusion that daylight should be excluded entirely and all work done under artificial lighting. Daylight is desirable and should be provided where possible, though in some cases it may be necessary to exclude windows for technical reasons, such as the need for a dust-free atmosphere with constant temperature and humidity.

Maintenance of lighting

The aims of good lighting will in time be defeated unless the lighting equipment and the structure of the building are well maintained. Cleanliness is of vital importance, particularly in modern lighting installations designed according to the principles of good lighting quality. If neglected, the lighting, whether daylight or artificial light, will no longer fulfil its purpose adequately, the relative cost of providing useful light will increase and the appearance of the building will suffer. Properly planned maintenance schedules are desirable for the room surfaces, the windows, and the artificial lighting equipment. All glazing should be cleaned both inside and outside at regular intervals, and suitable access should be provided. The efficiency of artificial lighting deteriorates with time for three main reasons, as follows.

• The light output from the lamps falls steadily throughout their life.

• Dust or other deposits, discolouration, or corrosion reduce the amount of light reflected or transmitted by the surfaces of the fittings.

• The reflectancies of the room surfaces become reduced because of dust or other deposits.

Lighting installations should be designed for ease of maintenance, and suitable access to the fittings and equipment should be provided. Good maintenance of equipment calls for regular servicing and cleaning of the fittings and for replacement of lamps when they have reached the end of their economically useful life. Lamps may be replaced individually or in groups, according to the type used. Group replacement offers advantages in some circumstances: for example, when the installation is large; when fittings are mounted at a considerable height or are otherwise inaccessible so that labour costs are high compared with the cost of the lamps; when access to the installation is possible only at long intervals because of the continuous nature of the task being lit; or when replacement of lamps can be combined with a planned scheme for cleaning the light fittings and for general maintenance.

Costs

Daylight is freely available out of doors, but certain costs are involved in admitting it to areas within a building. These may be regarded as the cost of daylight in comparison with artificial light. The more important items are the greater cost of windows compared with walls or roofing, the cost of losing internal heat through windows or roof glazing, the cost of providing shading or blinds to keep out direct sunlight in summer, and the cost of maintaining the windows during the life of the building. The cost of artificial lighting depends on the cost of the lamps and fittings, the luminous efficiency of the lamps, the cost of electricity, and the cost of maintenance. The initial and running costs of an artificial lighting installation must be related to the period of use. The initial cost is less important when the lighting is used continuously or nearly so; but when it is used only for short periods the initial cost is a significant part of the total, and an incandescent filament system may then have advantages over an initially more expensive fluorescent system. The different types of lamp are discussed more fully in the appendix at the end of this chapter.

Conclusions

Lighting technology has advanced considerably during recent years, especially in the study of the relation between people and the lighting they require for their work. Some commercial and industrial jobs can be undertaken satisfactorily in good general lighting, whereas for others this should be supplemented by tailored local lighting. A careful ergonomics appraisal of the situation should be made to determine the best form of lighting for the task. The aim should be to assess by direct experiment the light needed to do the task efficiently, and to design or select equipment to satisfy these requirements. In lighting design, the architect, the lighting engineer, and the ergonomist must collaborate at the design stage, rather than working independently. The general requirements for good work lighting can be summarised as follows.
(1) Up to a point, the eyes function better the more light they receive; beyond that point, glare supervenes. At least 200 lux should be provided for adequate visual performance at rough or unskilled work, and up to

2000 lux for difficult or fine work, when the work is being done continuously.

(2) The visual task should be brighter and more colourful than its surroundings. A moderate and comfortable level of general lighting should be provided, together with special lighting on the work.

(3) No source of light should cause glare discomfort. Artificial lighting fittings should be designed to minimise glare by preventing the light source from being visible to the person as the task is being performed. Windows may also be a source of discomfort glare, due to the sun or bright sky, and blinds or curtains will be required to reduce the glare.

(4) Daylight and artificial lighting should be properly integrated where used together to provide general lighting.

(5) Artificial light sources should be chosen to provide good colour rendering, especially when used during daylight hours or where a critical judgement of colours is required.

(6) Discharge lamps should be used with care to minimise flicker or stroboscopic effects.

(7) The lighting should allow work to proceed in comfort and with the minimum of visual and other physical fatigue.

(8) Adequate provision should be made for maintenance of all glazing, room surfaces, and light fittings.

(9) Maximum economy should be sought in the design, consistent with the effective functioning of the lighting.

(10) The scheme of decoration should be planned in conjunction with the lighting installation: the lighting of a building should always be considered in relation to its design and in particular to the scheme of decoration to be provided. On no account should lighting be considered merely as a matter of windows or light fittings: a good lighting installation is essentially concerned with the whole environment.

Appendix: Choice of electric lamps

The main types of electric lamps used in industry and elsewhere are the tubular fluorescent lamp, the high-pressure mercury discharge lamp (with and without metal halides added to the arc tube), and the high-pressure sodium discharge lamp. Some of them require a short period of time to achieve full light output after being switched on (run-up time); some lamps, on being switched off and then switched on again, require a period before restarting (restrike time).

Table 9.3 lists some of the most common types of lamp used, together with their main characteristics. These factors affect the choice of lamp for any particular installation, but it is also necessary to consider the initial costs of the lamps, fittings, and auxiliary gear, and the operating costs.

Advice on lighting problems can be obtained from manufacturers of lighting equipment and from the following organisations:

Building Research Station, Bucknalls Lane, Garston, Watford WD2 7JR. Tel: Garston (Herts) 674040.

Chartered Institution of Building Services, 222 Balham High Road, London SW12 9BS. Tel: 01-675-5211.

Table 9.3 Summary of lamp characteristics

Name of lamp type	Construction and appearance	Luminous efficacy (lm/W)	Life (hours)	Apparent colour	Colour rendering	Run-up time (min)	Restrike time (min)	Typical applications
Tungsten	A tungsten filament heated to incandescence in a glass envelope	8–18	1000–2000	Warm white light	Excellent	Immediate	Immediate	Social/commercial interiors such as hotel display lighting, emergency lighting, hand lamps
Tungsten–halogen	A tungsten filament heated to incandescence in a small envelope containing halogens	18–24	2000–4000	Warm white light	Excellent	Immediate	Immediate	Display lighting, area floodlighting
High-pressure mercury blended	An electric discharge in a high-pressure mercury atmosphere contained in an arc tube in series with a tungsten filament heated to incandescence; the whole contained within a glass envelope with a fluorescent coating	10–26	5000–8000	White light	Moderate	4	10	As a replacement for tungsten lamps where longer lamp life is essential
High-pressure mercury	An electric discharge in a high-pressure mercury atmosphere contained in an arc tube within a glass envelope with a fluorescent coating; needs control gear	36–54	5000–10 000	White light	Moderate	4	10	Industrial lighting, road lighting
Metal halide	An electric discharge in a high-pressure mercury atmosphere with metal halide additives in an arc tube, sometimes contained within a glass envelope; needs control gear	66–84	5000–10 000	Depends on the halogens used in the arc tube but tends to cold white light	Good	5	10	Industrial and commercial lighting, area floodlighting

Table 9.3 Summary of lamp characteristics (continued)

Name of lamp type	Construction and appearance	Luminous efficacy (lm/W)	Life (hours)	Apparent colour	Colour rendering	Run-up time (min)	Restrike time (min)	Typical applications
Tubular fluorescent	An electric discharge in a low-pressure mercury atmosphere contained in a glass tube internally coated with a fluorescent material; needs control gear	37–90	5000–10 000	Anything from warm white to cold white light	Anything from moderate to excellent depending on the properties of the fluorescent coating	Immediate	Immediate	Industrial and commercial lighting
High-pressure sodium	An electric discharge in a high-pressure sodium atmosphere in an arc tube contained in an outer envelope; needs control gear	67–121	6000–12 000	Slightly orange light	Poor	5	1	Industrial lighting, area floodlighting, road lighting
Low-pressure sodium	An electric discharge in a low-pressure sodium atmosphere in a glass arc tube contained in a glass envelope; needs control gear	101–175	6000–12 000	Yellow light	Non-existent	10	3	Road lighting, security lighting

Electricity Council (Marketing Department), 30 Millbank, London SW1P 4RD. Tel: 01-834-2333.
Lighting Industry Federation Ltd, 207 Balham High Road, London SW17 7BQ. Tel: 01-675-5432.

Further reading

BOYCE, P.R. (1981). *Human factors in lighting*. London: Applied Science Publishers.

CAYLESS, M.A. and MARSDEN, A.M. (1983). *Lamps and lighting*. London: Edward Arnold.

CHARTERED INSTITUTION OF BUILDING SERVICES (1984). *Code for interior lighting*. London: CIBS.

ELECTRICITY COUNCIL (1983). *Better office lighting*. London: The Electricity Council.

HOPKINSON, R.G. and COLLINS, J.B. (1970). *The ergonomics of lighting*. London: Macdonald and Co.

LIGHTING INDUSTRY FEDERATION LTD (1984). *Interior lighting design handbook*. London: The Lighting Industry Federation Ltd.

WESTON, H.C. (1962). *Sight, light and work*. London: H.K. Lewis and Co.

Chapter 10

Work organisation

In this chapter the factors which determine the ways in which tasks are organised into jobs are reviewed, the relationship between work and rest is discussed, and a description is given of how the load imposed on people by their jobs may be measured. Emphasis is placed on the distinction between physical workload and cognitive workload.

Introduction

This chapter differs from those that precede it, in that it does not present a series of definitive recommendations which may be followed when designing the hardware with which a person works or the environment in which the work is undertaken. This is because it deals with broader questions of how work is organised. The effectiveness with which a person can work, the satisfaction derived from it, and the degree to which it can be safely undertaken, are not just products of the equipment used and the environmental conditions. They are also products of the way tasks are allocated to people, what control they have over the work being undertaken, the time allocated to do the work, etc. It is to these aspects of work organisation that this chapter is addressed.

Topics of work organisation have been addressed by ergonomists who have, for example, been concerned with shift work and work/rest pause arrangements, and also by social scientists who, under the heading of job design, have considered how work is organised into jobs and how jobs are related to one another. It is not the intention to offer a detailed coverage of social-science topics, but it is appropriate to include a list of work organisation issues which span the two disciplines, in order to show how they interact.

The best way of organising work is usually a product of general principles interpreted according to local customs and history and the objectives and needs of employees. The ergonomist cannot work, therefore, by prescribing a solution, but must work as a change agent, offering options and principles and helping people to select an appropriate solution for themselves. This procedure is followed in this chapter. Principles and options are outlined with some of their advantages and disadvantages, but very few definitive recommendations are made.

Division of labour and the design of jobs

An organisation with a large task to undertake, such as building a motor car, works by dividing the task into small tasks and allocating them to employees. One of the principles by which this division of labour has occurred in the past has been to find the smallest, simplest component tasks, allocate each to a separate person, and introduce complex control and co-ordination mechanisms to ensure that all the parts fit together. This task specialisation approach has been widely criticised for producing narrow, repetitive, rigidly controlled jobs which neither provide people with the opportunity to fulfill their potential nor provide them with job satisfaction.

In the light of this, there have been many attempts to define what might constitute a 'good' job. The central principle is to provide a person with autonomy appropriate to responsibilities and abilities. This can be developed into the following specific principles.
- A job should be reasonably demanding in mental terms, and should provide variety.
- The person should be able to learn continuously on the job.
- The person should have at least some minimal area of decision-making.
- The person's efforts and accomplishments should be recognised in the workplace.
- It should be possible to relate work to life outside work (ie to feel that the job is significant and meaningful).
- It should be possible to feel that the job leads to some sort of desirable future (not necessarily promotion).

None of these principles is absolute. Some may be more important in some situations, whilst others are critical elsewhere. It is always a question of interpreting the list according to local traditions and needs.

Combining tasks into jobs

Many of these principles are concerned with the way tasks are put together to form the job responsibilities of a person. A number of strategies have been proposed for doing this in a way which will meet the needs of the person for worthwhile work and of the organisation for effective task performance. If we assume we are moving away from a narrow form of task specialisation they may be listed as follows.

Job rotation
This involves regular staff movement from one task to another. This is useful if each task is boring: it adds variety and a wider perspective, but the tasks need to relate to one another. It is also useful if some of the tasks are disliked more than others.

An example of where job rotation could be used would be a chocolate-making line with five stations for loading a hopper with chocolate centres, operating a chocolate coating machine, inspecting for rejects, operating a wrapping machine, and boxing the chocolates. A job rotation scheme whereby each operative rotated through these five positions, spending one or two hours at each post, would add variety, mix the more active and passive activities, and give a more complete perspective on the entire operation.

Job enlargement (or horizontal job design)
In this case, tasks are added to the job to provide more variety. However, unless the tasks add discretion and responsibility, as described below, the gain will only be in variety.

If we took the example of the chocolate-wrapping machine operator described above, job enlargement might consist of collecting stocks of wrappers from the stores, completing simple maintenance tasks on the machine, having responsibility for keeping the area clean, safe, and hygienic, etc. Each of these tasks adds to the variety of the work without noticeably increasing autonomy or discretion.

Job enrichment (or vertical job design)
Tasks in this case are allocated to the job so that the person has responsibility for all the tasks necessary to complete a major subgoal. This approach adds variety and autonomy to the job.

There are many examples of job enrichment in manufacturing, but an example from the service sector may indicate that the principles can be applied to many different types of jobs. In ICI, laboratory technicians were given job enrichment by being required to write up the results of tests they had run, being given authority to re-order stocks of depleted chemicals, and having an opportunity to undertake some exploratory studies of their own devising. Each change added to their area of autonomy, and gave more complete control over an integrated set of duties.

Semi-autonomous work groups
In this scheme, mostly associated with socio-technical systems design, a group of employees is given responsibility for a large task, eg the operation of a chemical plant, and has the autonomy to decide who will undertake which of the component tasks. The group size is normally restricted to 10 in order to sustain good face-to-face communication between its members.

When semi-automatic looms were introduced into an Indian weaving shed, the old system of one weaver per loom was no longer possible. Instead a semi-autonomous work group structure was created with teams of seven being responsible for a number of looms. Each team consisted of weavers and maintenance staff so that it could be autonomous in the setting up, running, and maintaining of the looms under its control. The group members could allocate duties amongst themselves as they deemed appropriate, and needed very little external direction or supervision.

Decisions about which of these schemes, or their variants, to select are dependent upon many factors. Individual job design schemes are best suited to circumstances in which tasks are largely independent and can be undertaken by one person. Where a wide range of tasks is highly interdependent, a team approach such as semi-autonomous work groups may be more appropriate. If the previous work arrangement has been based upon task specialisation, the easiest scheme to introduce is job rotation, because it involves the least radical change in working arrangements. Schemes such as job enrichment and semi-autonomous work groups may change the roles of associated employees: foremen and first line management would need to devolve decision making to employees, and maintenance and inspection staff may find employees engaging in some of these activities for themselves. Job rotation and job enlargement do not involve these broader organisational changes but, in contrast, are not likely to be perceived as particularly beneficial by employees or management. It is almost inevitable that the major benefits are only obtained as a result of major change and disruption. The principal benefits of these schemes are greater job satisfaction on the part of employees and greater flexibility and quality of work for the organisation. Typically there is also a short term versus long term trade off. A highly supervised and controlled task specialisation arrangement may get today's work completed quickly, but only a scheme that gives a measure of responsibility and autonomy to individual employees will enable them to develop into the resourceful, skilled members of staff who can help cope with the new demands of tomorrow. Another issue is the expectations of the workforce. It might be expected that they would welcome opportunities for greater autonomy, variety, and job satisfaction. However, in many circumstances, employees may feel threatened by these opportunities and may prefer the present uninteresting but familiar work arrangements. They may also be suspicious of the motives behind the change, or may seek other goals: for example, more money for more responsibility.

It will be seen from these issues that there is no one universal solution to the problem of work organisation, and that the decision has to be based upon the nature of the work to be undertaken, the nature of human motivation, and the current values and goals of workforce and management. The ergonomist engaged in work design needs to be able to bring all these issues to the attention of both management and workforce so that they can make appropriate decisions.

The list of further reading at the end of this chapter provides many case study examples of these schemes and detailed methodological guidance about their implementation.

Work organisation and the physical nature of man

Job design is normally perceived as a process of marrying the needs of an organisation with the psycho-social needs of people, eg their motives and aspirations individually and collectively. The process of establishing a form of work organisation must, however, also take account of people as biological entities, and must consider their cognitive capacities and characteristics when it involves information processing effort. These characteristics affect the degree to which a person can produce a steady work output over time. People are not like machines which can be turned on, and which will produce a steady output until switched off. The human organism varies in output capability over time and with the conditions under which the work is being undertaken. Work organisation must recognise these characteristics and seek to optimise the opportunity to work effectively. In an age of automation, these special requirements may seem to put people at a disadvantage when compared with increasingly sophisticated machines, but they also have an advantage. The machine may work steadily once switched on but is subject to sudden, possibly calamitous, performance failure in the event of a breakdown. People, by contrast, when placed under stress tend not to show a sudden loss of performance but to display 'graceful degradation'—progressively less able performance, but the maintenance of viable output for a long period whilst corrective action may be taken.

In this section we examine a number of work organisation issues which are directly affected by the physical nature of man. The resolution of these issues is sometimes independent of the 'tasks into jobs' issues considered in job design. The issues are concerned with workload and rhythm and the control the individual has over these issues under different work organisation regimes.

Workload and performance

To make judgements about the forms of work organisation required because of different workloads, we need ways of assessing workload. This is one of the major problems in ergonomics. Where work involves heavy physical labour, the energy required can be assessed, and the effects of maintaining this level of output over time can be calculated. As technology increasingly takes over the energy expenditure tasks, human work is becoming largely characterised by information processing. It is much more difficult to assess the cognitive 'work' being undertaken in these tasks. It remains true, however, that in both cases the person can be overloaded by too great a demand, and can become fatigued and prone to error when engaged in the task for too long a period without resting. It is therefore important in the cases of both physical and mental work to try to establish workload and relate it to performance. In this section, therefore, we begin by discussing the measurement issues for both physical and cognitive work, and then consider the implications for work/rest regimes and for pacing and other aspects of controlling workload.

Heavy physical work

The energy expended in physical work is measured in kilocalories (kcal). One kcal = 4 btu (British thermal unit). Since the energy produced by muscle contraction is directly related to the oxygen used (the exact relationship depending on the proportion of carbohydrate, protein, and fat in the diet), energy expended may be measured by ascertaining the oxygen consumed and the carbon dioxide produced. Equipment for this purpose will therefore be required to measure the ventilation rate in cubic metres (m^3), and to take a sample of the expired air for subsequent gas analysis. Apparatus which has been used in industry for this purpose includes the Kofranyi–Michaelis gas meter, which has a high resistance to even moderate ventilation rates, and the Integrating Pneumotachograph (IMP). Both these devices have the disadvantage that they are bulky and require the subject to wear a mask over the face. Moreover, they can give only a coarse picture of the pattern of physical activity of the operative.

The second method of measurement is more practically viable for industry. This depends on the fact that, for any one individual, the elevation of heart rate above the resting level is fairly closely related to the energy expended (Fig 10.1).

Heart rate may be measured by stopping the work for 15 seconds and palpating the wrist, by picking up potentials from the heart by means of suitably placed electrodes, or by detecting differences in tissue density by a photoelectric method. Palpation of the wrist requires no special equipment other than a watch. Equipment for the photoelectric measurement of heart rate is available commercially which picks up signals either from the finger or the leg or the earlobe. This type of cardiotachometer, which is light and portable, has to be carried on the person of the operative and must be read for spot values at required intervals by the investigator. Several methods of utilising signals from electrodes placed in the region of the heart are available. If the subject is static, the leads can be connected directly into a cardiotachometer, which, in addition to showing the rate on a meter, will give a voltage proportional to the rate for feeding into a suitable recorder, such as a potentiometric recorder.

Some techniques of work assessment depend on counting the total number of beats in a particular period of time. This can either be done by reading a counter, which may be an integral part of the equipment, or by feeding pulses into a printout counter set to print at predetermined time intervals. If the operative is mobile, the heart pulses can be telemetered to a suitable receiver, whence they are fed into a cardiotachometer as described above.

Information-processing work
The methods described above are of little value in measuring work which is predominantly mental in character. Various techniques have been proposed to assess the mental load under which a person is working. One of

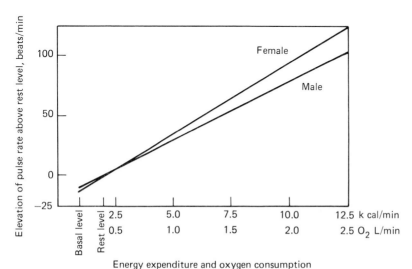

Figure 10.1 Relation between pulse rate and energy expenditure.

the most reliable is secondary task assessment, in which the subject is asked to undertake two tasks simultaneously: the primary task and a second task such as mental arithmetic. Performance on the second task is used to assess the spare mental capacity remaining after performance of the primary task. This technique is useful for measuring how close to peak capacity a person is working, since secondary task performance degrades quickly when the person is experiencing the primary task as very demanding.

Assessing workload over a period of time rather than looking just for peaks in workload is usually done directly in terms of performance measures using quantity (such as key strokes in keying tasks) and quality measures (such as accuracy and errors). These measures must be developed in relation to the targets of specific tasks. It is usually easier to assess routine, repetitive tasks than unstructured problem-solving tasks because the repetition of cycles of activity allows a log of comparable performance to be maintained which will show whether performance is stable, improving, or deteriorating. Measures taken in this way of continuous performance show a typical pattern. There is a warm-up period in which the person is adjusting to the task, a period of peak performance, and then a gradual decline as more errors are made, quality falls, and output becomes less regular. The period of peak performance is known as the actile period. An example is given in Fig 10.2, where the task is to extinguish a light being illuminated in different areas of the periphery of vision at random intervals. The end of the actile period is approximately 70 minutes, when the time taken becomes appreciably longer and errors begin to appear.

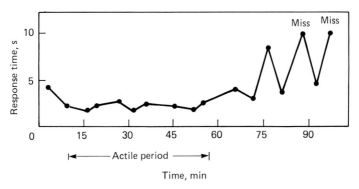

Figure 10.2 Plot of time taken to see and extinguish a peripheral light.

Work/rest schedules

Measurement of both physical and mental work performance shows that human beings cannot sustain long periods of peak output without taking a rest. The optimum point to rest is just before performance begins to deteriorate, which means measuring techniques are necessary to establish this point. Once again methods for doing this are more easily established for physical work than for cognitive work.

Physical work
When work is sufficiently heavy, the methods of oxygen consumption or heart rate measurement, already described, can be used to assess what rest pauses are needed and how often. For practical purposes in industry, measurement must be related to an 'average man', and this has been agreed internationally as being an individual with a stature of 175 cm, a weight of 65 kg and a body surface area of 1.77 m^2. This average man can work at 5 kcal/min for a reasonable period of time without building up an oxygen debt. However, if the work exceeds 5 kcal/min, an oxygen debt will be built up which appears to be in two stages. If rest is taken at the end of the first stage, rest requirement is minimal, but if work continues beyond this optimal point the rest required becomes disproportionately longer.

For practical purposes it would seem that the length of working time (TW) can be calculated as

$$TW = \frac{25}{x - 5}$$

where x is the level of energy expenditure in kilocalories. The time of recovery (TR) is given by

$$TR = \frac{25}{5 - a}$$

where a is energy expenditure in kilocalories during recovery.

Thus, if $x = 6$ kcal/min and, where the operative rests completely, $a = 1.5$ kcal/min, then the optimum work/rest schedule would be 25 min work and 7 min rest. In practice this could probably be modified to 24 min work and 6 min rest without any adverse effects. It will be appreciated from these formulae that if short periods of heavy and light work are dispersed in the proper proportion, so that the overall energy expenditure is kept below 5 kcal/min, then the requirements for rest are minimal.

If the heart rate is used as an index of workload, it will be found that, for the average individual, mean heart rate level will remain steady over a working shift provided it does not rise during work phases above the resting rate plus 30, which level is roughly equivalent to 5 kcal/min. Rest requirement is usually measured by pulse recovery time (PRT), the time required for the pulse to return to the resting level. If the mean heart rate is maintained at or below the steady level (Fig 10.3), the PRT is independent of the length of time that the work has continued, within wide limits.

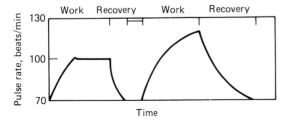

Figure 10.3 Pulse rate curves for moderate and heavy work of the same duration.

If the work is sufficiently heavy to cause the heart rate to rise conti- nuously, then the optimum PRT will be related to the length of the working period, as described above for kilocalorie measurements. If the PRT is insufficient, the next bout of work will raise the heart rate even higher (Fig 10.4), and if insufficient rest is again taken, it will rise still further until the point of exhaustion is reached. If rest pauses are not taken at the appropriate time the penalty is again high, in that if the length of the work phase is doubled the PRT goes up by about 3.5 times.

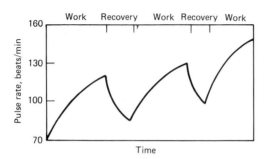

Figure 10.4 Pulse rate curve when recovery is inadequate in heavy work.

Information-processing work

In information-processing work the person also becomes fatigued or con- centration lapses after a period of time, although, unlike physical work, it is difficult to measure what cognitive resources are being drained. The aim therefore would be to assess the actile period and introduce rest pauses just before the onset of performance degradation.

Where this has been done, particularly for relatively repetitive clerical work, the actile period is often in the 1 hour to 1.5 hour range. This would indicate a break every hour, which is more frequent than the industrial practice of breaks mid-morning, lunch, and mid-afternoon. However, such patterns have been shown to increase productivity and quality. In one firm it has been reported that, when 10-minute rests in every hour were introduced, rejects were reduced to one fifth of their previous level and production increased by more than 10%.

The nature of the rest break is also important if it is to facilitate a return to good performance. In the case of mental work, if the breaks are frequent they need not be long. The 10 minutes quoted above is ample. The most important feature is to move away from the place of work to another location. Information-processing work, especially in the increas- ingly common context of operating visual display units, keeps people in physically constrained postures in circumstances where there may be visual strain, and in socially isolated conditions. A temporary move to another location may shift the muscular load, allow the eyes to rest, and provide opportunities for social interaction. It is conventional for rest pauses to include drinks and snacks, and research has been undertaken to establish whether these are instrumental in returning to good performance. The conclusion is that it is the change of activity and scene which makes the difference, rather than the refreshment.

The issue of rest pauses is one where there is a potential conflict between the conclusions about people as biological entities and conclusions about their psycho-social characters. The findings reported above would suggest that, in any work setting, it would be possible to establish an optimum work/rest schedule. In many organisations this is a subject for industrial relations negotiations, and scientific findings which might provide the basis for an agreement are often seen as attractive. It is, however, likely that such agreements would be applied widely across many work settings, and they may be enforced, requiring people to take breaks at set points during the day. However, it is a matter of common experience, widely supported by research evidence, that people seek 'psychological closure' in the tasks they undertake. Tasks are goal directed, and when goals are attained there is a sense of achievement and a clearing of the memory banks of data relating to that activity in readiness to engage in another task. It can be very frustrating to be interrupted 'in full flow', especially when the task is nearing completion. It can also be counterproductive in performance terms, because the task performer 'loses track' of the point in the task being undertaken and has to spend extra time in re-orientation. To have to stop in the middle of a task episode because of a rigid work/rest schedule can seem very foolish and irritating to people at work. It should be possible, therefore, for people to stop when they reach a natural break in their activities. There are of course highly motivated people who will continue with an engrossing task much longer than is desirable for their physical wellbeing and long after they have ceased to operate at peak performance. It cannot therefore simply be left to people to take a break when they are ready for it. This is an area where the ergonomist cannot prescribe a solution but must inform management, unions, and the work-force of the relevant principles so that they may use their own discretion to develop working patterns appropriate to their wellbeing and to successful task performance.

Work rhythms and pacing

It is in the nature of human work that it varies in rate over time. As the actile period studies show (see Fig 10.2) there is a tendency to start slowly, develop a peak flow which has a steady rhythm to it, and then to lose this rhythm as fatigue develops. There are then variations in any individual in the rate of work. There are likely to be even greater variations over the course of a day's work: beginning slowly, developing to a peak, perhaps with a slow period after lunch, and a winding down at the end of the day. There can also be individual variations over longer time spans as a result of learning and becoming more proficient at the task, because of the general state of health and, ultimately, because of ageing.

There will also be large differences in rates of output between people, because of differences in skill and aptitude, motivation, age, etc. There may also be differences in the rhythms they display, some working better in the morning than in the afternoon, for example. This description of human variability is presented because good forms of work organisation will allow people to work to their own best rhythms and pace. There are, however, many forces in the work setting which can act to set the pace for people on a minute-by-minute basis. One of the most significant forms of stress at work is pacing stress, when one is forced to act at a rate maybe faster, maybe slower, than one's natural rhythm and when a break cannot be taken at the point when it is required. Matching work to one's own natural rhythm is likely to produce more work and better results in the long term than being forced to operate at an externally enforced pace.

It is useful to distinguish three different forms of minute by minute pacing, as follows.

(1) *Pacing by machine.* The most common form of pacing is the paced assembly line, which gives each operator a limited time in which to undertake the relevant task. This form of pacing is usually centrally controlled, with many sequentially interdependent tasks driven by the rate set. This arrangement is not only stressful to the human condition but can also be very inflexible: a problem at one point in the line can bring the complete sequence to a halt. These considerations have driven some manufacturing organisations who have traditionally relied upon paced assembly lines to abandon them in favour of semi-autonomous work groups who are able to set their own pace. The best-known example is Volvo in Sweden, who have invested in a completely new plant using the work group principle. It is not in assembly lines alone that machine pacing can occur. It can also occur in process plants, in vehicle control tasks, and in other tasks which have to be undertaken in a limited time frame whilst some machine-initiated process is taking place. The most important consideration in such circumstances, which is achievable in most of them, is that there should be local control over the machine so that its rate of operation can be attuned to the rate at which the person wishes to work.

(2) *Pacing in interdependent tasks.* When a group of people work together on a set of tasks which are sequentially interdependent, ie one must be completed before the next can begin, pacing can result even when no machines are involved. This is because the rate at which the first person works defines how quickly the second person can work, and so on down the line, with the result that the whole sequence is performed at the rate of the slowest operation. This problem can be ameliorated by placing a buffer between each workstation, ie a stock of items for each person to work on so that they are not dependent upon the people who precede them. In one study of girls assembling television sets without a buffer between them, it was found that there was 18% lost time; this was reduced to 4% when one set was placed between every other girl and the line of 100 girls was broken down into four groups of 25. The time saving from further increasing the buffer size was less than the cost of the additional floor space required, and of the increased cost of work in progress.

(3) *Pacing from external sources.* Sometimes the source of pacing is external. This is particularly the case in service organisations, where customers and clients may form queues or make simultaneous demands on service-giving personnel. Often these forms of pacing occupy short periods of peak demand, eg ticket collectors when a train arrives in a station. Short-lived peaks require flexible manning arrangements so that maximum resources are available to meet maximum demand. Where the demand is paced and continuous, the person needs to be able to build in a break when it is required if he or she is to sustain the pace, ie to be able to select when

they are ready to receive the next customer rather than to be automatically confronted by one when the previous one has been dealt with.

The most common techniques for controlling pacing, therefore, are to allow people local control over the rate of work, or to provide buffers so that people can organise themselves without being controlled by the rate at which others work.

It is important in considering pacing issues to distinguish between end-pressures (deadlines by which a volume of work has to be complete) and minute-by-minute pacing. The end result in terms of amount of work completed may be exactly the same but, in human terms, the two conditions are very different. Minute-by-minute pacing controls and standardises the rhythm of the work and can take little account of intra- or inter-individual variations. An end target allows each person to organise him/herself, possibly using quite different strategies, to get through the volume of work in his or her own way.

It should be noted that, in this case, the findings that arise from studies of people as physical and as psycho-social organisms point in the same direction; both indicate the need for autonomy to allow people to organise themselves to take account of their particular characteristics and aspirations.

Bodily rhythms and shift work

Work rhythms are not simply short-term issues arising from the effects of prolonged work. There are also well-documented cycles in bodily functions, which have important consequences for work organisation, especially shift work. Body functions do not remain constant throughout the 24 hours, but vary in what is known as the circadian rhythm between a low at about 04.00 hours rising to a maximum at about 20.00 hours (Fig 10.5). During the periods of low activity most bodily functions are decreased, the temperature is at its lowest, mental activity diminishes, digestion slows down, and the secretion of urine is reduced—all of which is conducive to a good night's sleep. At the other phase of the rhythm the reverse is the case and the body is most active, a condition which is favourable for work. The most readily measured of these functions is the body temperature, which varies by about 2.5°C.

If an individual is on permanent night-shift, the circadian rhythm may be almost exactly the opposite to that of a person on day-shift. Should there

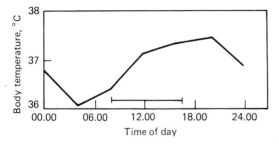

Figure 10.5 Circadian variation in body temperature.

be a change in shift pattern, as when transferring from day-shift to night-shift, the circadian rhythm will change, in most people, to be in accordance with the new activity pattern. In some people this inversion may be achieved in four or five days; in others there may be no change at all over a substantial period of time. Thus, at the beginning of any period of night-shift, a person may be trying to work when the body wishes to sleep, and trying to sleep when the body is most active. Reversion back to a day-work rhythm is very much more rapid at the end of a period on nights. Studies of sleep deprivation have suggested that with up to two days of inadequate sleep, performance may be relatively little impaired, but beyond this, until inversion is achieved, there will be a reduction in performance. This suggests that short periods on nights are likely to be more satisfactory than somewhat longer periods of, say, seven shifts, when the person may go back on to day-shift just when adaptation to night working has been achieved.

Research into the effects of circadian rhythm on night work have suggested the following.

• Production on night-shift is lower than that on the morning shift for about the first four weeks on continuous night-shift.

• Absenteeism is higher on the morning shift immediately following periods on night-shift.

• Absenteeism during the second week of a two-week night-shift system is greater than absence in the first week.

• Absenteeism on the night-shift is generally less than on the day-shift, and, on a four-week system, is about half the absenteeism on a two-week system.

• Inversion is likely to take place quicker in an active job than in a job which is mainly inactive.

• Process workers working on nights for a week at a time made about 100% more errors in logging at about 04.00 h than during the morning and afternoon shifts.

Factors which have to be taken into account when deciding what shift system to use are biological, technical, and social, and whether shifts are continuous or run on a weekly basis.

• For biological reasons, shift systems should either be very short (two or three days), or quite long (minimum four weeks).

• For technological reasons, shift systems will be determined by the demands of the process and of information handover, and will have to be determined in each particular case.

• For social reasons, shift systems should either be very short, when they will interfere very little with regular social activity, or be permanent when part of the community can come to terms with living on a fixed routine.

• Both continuous and weekly shift systems are influenced by reversion during the weekend, although this effect is diminished by longer periods on the same shift.

The evidence suggests that the most satisfactory system is likely to be one in which quite short periods are worked on each shift. Typical systems are described in Fig 10.6.

Continuous shifts

	Su	M	T	W	Th	F	S	Su	M	T	
2-2-2											
A		1	1	2	2	3	3	0	0		
B		2	2	3	3	0	0	1	1		
C		3	3	0	0	1	1	2	2		
D		0	0	1	1	2	2	3	3	etc.	
2-2-3											
A		1	1	2	2	3	3	3	0	0	
B		2	2	3	3	0	0	0	1	1	
C		3	3	0	0	1	1	1	2	2	
D		0	0	1	1	2	2	2	3	3	etc.

Shifts

1 = 06 - 14 h
2 = 14 - 22 h
3 = 22 - 06 h

Weekly shifts

	Su	M	T	W	Th	F	S	Su	M	T	
2-3											
A	3	3	0	1	1	1	0	0	2	2	
B	0	1	1	2	2	2	0	3	3	0	
C	0	2	2	3	3	3	0	0	1	1	etc.

The number of rest periods in 24 weeks

	periods	hours duration
2-2-2 system	21	48
2-2-3 system	12	48
	6	72
2-3 system	16	72
	8	48
	8	24

Figure 10.6 Typical systems of short-period shift work.

For continuous shifts the 2–2–3 shift system seems to be preferred because of the 'long weekend' of 72 hours which occurs once in every four weeks. Firms which have changed over to this system claim a big improvement in the health of their shift workers.

This is again an area where the findings from biological studies seem to point in the same direction as psycho-social studies. They are not, however, in accord with traditional practice, which views the weekly cycle as the 'natural' cycle although it is the most unnatural for people.

Conclusions

In this chapter a review is given of a variety of factors which can affect the form of work organisation that may be appropriate in a specific situation. A variety of possible forms of work organisation are also examined. In conclusion, a summary of these factors and forms is presented, and other issues which may affect work organisation are identified.

The factors that affect work organisation discussed in this chapter are social, cognitive, and physical. In addition to the variables under these headings discussed above, there are others that are often deserving of attention, as follows.

Social factors. There are many strong cultural and traditional work patterns which will create expectations amongst management and the work force about the way work will be organised. In Scandinavia, for example, there is a much greater emphasis upon democratisation of the workplace than in Great Britain. As a result, it has proved much easier to implement semi-autonomous work groups in Scandinavia.

Cognitive factors. It is often assumed that people at work learn whilst they are being trained, achieve an adequate level of performance, and remain at that level thereafter. This is patently untrue, and research has shown that even when undertaking repetitive and undemanding tasks people continue to learn and as a result refine their work strategies to achieve their objectives more quickly with better control of quality or less expenditure of effort. This natural benefit from employing self-organising, adaptive work performers can be lost if the form of work organisation does not permit people to adjust their work strategies over time.

Physical factors. In addition to the physical factors that have been discussed, there are others that can affect work organisation. As people age, their physical capacities may diminish and they may not be able to work as quickly. However, they have a reservoir of experience not available to younger colleagues, and can often find work strategies which compensate for any loss of physical capability. Similarly, disabled people may be able to find ways of working which enable them to work alongside able-bodied colleagues. Such adaptive behaviour may be inhibited by a heavily structured form of work organisation. Pacing, in particular, often prevents the older worker and the disabled from performing effectively. One virtue of group structures is that often the members of the group are able to work out ways of allocating themselves to allow for both strengths and weaknesses, such that, for example, as people age, they occupy different roles within the group.

Several forms of work organisation are identified above, but many others are possible. The important dimensions upon which they vary are as follows.

• The *content* of the work is largely defined by the way in which tasks are allocated to jobs and those jobs to people. Forms of work organisation can vary from the narrow single task type of job to the integrated multi-task kind of job.

• The *autonomy* associated with the work can vary from the highly structured, paced forms of work organisation to forms in which, within

broad policies and objectives, an individual or a group has discretion to establish patterns of work.
- The *period of work to period of rest* or leisure is also an important variable. In the short term there are alternative work/rest pause schedules, and in the longer term there are shift work arrangements.

The decision about the appropriate form of work organisation for a particular group of employees depends upon many variables, and will ideally be made by consultation with all the people involved. Although the conclusions from research on people from a social, cognitive, and physical perspective may at times be in conflict, there is one underlying conclusion towards which all the research leads. Given the variety shown by people at work, both between individuals and in the same individual over time, the most important feature to be found in any form of work organisation is a degree of flexibility which can be used to take advantage of the variability. This is in conflict with the strong tradition of scientific management in many organisations, which puts emphasis upon tight control in order to produce high-quality, standardised performance. This approach has been shown many times to be based upon an inadequate view of the nature of people, and the forms of work organisation discussed in this chapter, which provide some measure of flexibility, can help each person create work patterns which match personal characteristics which can in turn lead to superior performance.

Further reading

Job design

DAVIS, L.E. and CHERNS, A.B. (1975). *The quality of working life*. Free Press
DAVIS, L.E. and TAYLOR, J.C. (eds) (1972). *Design of jobs*. London: Penguin
KLEIN, L. (1976). *New forms of work organisation*. London: Cambridge University Press
RICE, A.K. (1958). *Productivity and social organisation: the Ahmedabad experiment*. Tavistock
WARR, P.B. and WALL, T. (1975). *Work and well being*. London: Penguin

Workload, pacing, and shift work

CONRAD, R. (1969). In Holding, D.H. (ed) *Experimental psychology in industry*. London: Penguin. 'Speed stress'
CORLETT, E.N. and RICHARDSON, J. (eds) (1981). *Stress, work design and productivity*. Chichester: Wiley
MURRELL, K.F.H. (1965). *Ergonomics*. London: Chapman and Hall
MURRELL, K.F.H. (1969). In Holding, D.H. (ed) *Experimental psychology in industry*. London: Penguin. 'Industrial aspects of ageing'
POULTON, E.C. (1978). In Warr, P.B. (ed) *Psychology at work*. London: Penguin. 'Workload and skilled performance'
WILKINSON, R.T. (1976). In Warr, P.B. (ed) *Psychology at work*. London: Penguin. 'Hours of work and the twenty-four-hour cycle of rest and activity'

Chapter 11

Case studies of the application of ergonomics

The purpose of this chapter is to illustrate in greater detail some of the principles and methods that have been described in the previous chapters.

In Chapters 1 to 10 of this book we have explained and discussed the main areas of study of ergonomics as an applied discipline. We have considered the basic models of people, machines, and environments, and have looked more closely at the design of controls and displays, the ways in which they are integrated, the design of workstations, and the effects of various environmental factors on human performance.

A number of examples have been given in the previous chapters to underline the relevance and importance of the points being made. However, these necessarily have been brief. This chapter contains a selection of more detailed examples of the application of ergonomics, and is intended to show more clearly how ergonomics methods and data can be used to make the equipment and facilities we use safer, easier, more efficient, and more pleasant to work with.

The chapter contains reports of four investigations. All of these have been recently published in the journal *Applied Ergonomics* and are reprinted here in their published form, together with a short preliminary comment to help the reader identify the rationale and methods used in them and to set them in context.

The four investigations are concerned with the following topics:

● the modification of industrial equipment and environments to improve the health and performance of factory workers;
● the assessment of safe handling temperatures, principally for domestic materials;
● the value of education in ergonomics amongst industrial supervisors;
● the contribution made by ergonomics in the design of communications systems.

These examples clearly are not exhaustive in covering the areas of application of ergonomics; neither is each 'complete' in the sense of using, for example, all types of measurement methods, or of addressing all the components of a user–machine system (controls and displays, workplaces, physical environment, and psychological environment). This is not surprising: as we have seen, certain study and measurement methods are inappropriate for certain problems; it is sometimes impossible to study all the

Example 1   157

components of a user–machine system, because of constraints of time and money or because some components are outside the control of the agency commissioning the work; and, since ergonomics can be applied to virtually any user–machine system, it is inevitable that some areas of application will be missed out in a selection of just four studies. Nevertheless, the four presented here should give the reader a good idea of the range of applications of ergonomics, and further examples can readily be found by consulting the journal *Applied Ergonomics*.

Example 1

R.H. Westgaard and A. Aaras: Postural muscle strain as a causal factor in the development of musculo-skeletal illnesses. 1984 *Applied Ergonomics*, volume 15, number 3, pp 162–174.
R.H. Westgaard and A. Aaras: The effect of improved workplace design on the development of work-related musculo-skeletal illnesses. 1985 *Applied Ergonomics*, volume 16, number 2, pp 91–97.
Two articles are reprinted for this example, as they are closely related. Together, they describe a study whose data cover a period of about 13 years. It is unusual and gratifying to find such long-term studies; they are difficult to organise and are rather expensive, although their results are often more revealing than shorter investigations. The study deals with the application of ergonomics to solve, or at least to reduce, an occupational health problem in a small factory in Norway where people are employed to assemble electrical components by hand.

The authors start by identifying the main symptoms of the problem: these are the occurrence of disorders in the muscles and skeleton, and are manifested in periods of absence through sickness. Other symptoms include reports of pain and discomfort by the workers, a high turnover of the labour force, and low productivity in the company as a whole. The authors establish the relationship between muscular strain and illness, and look for evidence of illness as an index of strain. After an analysis of the working conditions in the factory and of the equipment used, they introduce a series of simple and straightforward modifications based on ergonomics principles so as to make the workplace more comfortable and less likely to lead to poor posture and, subsequently, pain and discomfort. The measures that were taken before the modifications were introduced were repeated some time after, and the results show reductions in the incidence of illness, the level of labour turnover, and reports of pain and discomfort, together with an increase in the productivity of the workers. In addition, the authors make a direct comparison of the 'before' and 'after' workplace designs by means of electromyography. This is the measurement of the electrical activity of the muscles; the higher the level of this activity, the more it can be said that the muscle is under stress. The advantages of the new designs over the old ones are demonstrated by this form of measurement.

The first article describes the general structure of the factory as well as presenting data on absence due to sickness, reports of pain and discomfort (which may or may not involve a visit to a doctor and subsequent sick leave), and labour turnover. Comparisons are also made with workers in other industries to assert that a definite problem existed in the factory. The article also describes the changes made to workplace design, equipment, and lighting of the task. The second article continues by describing the electromyographic data, presenting the post-modification data, and comparing them with the initial data.

Field studies of this sort are difficult to carry out because the effects noted may not necessarily be due to the changes made to equipment or procedures, but rather to other, concurrent changes outside the scope of the study, such as legislation in health and safety, the level of national employment, changes in management style, and so forth. In other words, field studies are difficult or impossible to control. Despite this, the authors take considerable trouble to isolate the various causes of the improvements noted, and their argument is convincing.

The authors also illustrate an important point about the effectiveness of ergonomics-based solutions in an industrial environment: this is that although it may be difficult or impossible completely to eliminate a problem, considerable benefit may accrue from reducing it. In the study, neither illness nor sick leave attributable to musculo-skeletal disorders was eliminated: but the reductions observed were significant, and the productivity of the workers was improved. The practising ergonomist has always to realise that a compromise must be reached between the 'ideal' ergonomics solution and what is possible under financial, technical, and managerial constraints.

See page 162 for the articles, which are reproduced in full from *Applied Ergonomics*.

Example 2

R.D. Ray: The theory and practice of safe handling temperatures. 1984 *Applied Ergonomics*, volume 15, number 1, pp 55–59.
Most of us have at one time or another burned ourselves on a saucepan handle or an oven door. Less seriously, we often find that we can hold a hot handle for only a short time before it becomes uncomfortable. Manufacturers recognise these problems and attempt to design their products so that they do not get so hot as to cause burns or discomfort. The ideal solution might be to ensure that no components become even warm, let alone hot, but this would be difficult and expensive. So information is needed about temperatures of surfaces that are tolerable when touched or held, but which would not be prohibitively expensive to make. What should these temperatures be?

The author sets out to answer this question. It is not an easy task because, in addition to the temperature of the surface being touched or handled, we must also consider the temperature of the part of the body in contact with the surface, and the type of material being touched: a piece of wood at a certain temperature, for example, will be tolerable to touch for longer than a piece of metal at the same temperature. This difference is expressed in terms of different values of a 'contact coefficient'.

The author establishes first that burns from domestic equipment are a

ᵃᵃ
Example 3   159

big enough problem to warrant an investigation, by reference to hospital data. After outlining the effects of heat on the body, he discusses the physics of heat transfer to produce an equation which in theory should predict a safe surface temperature in terms of skin temperature, contact coefficients of the skin and the surface, and the contact temperature (the temperature at the point of contact between skin and surface which has stabilised after the transfer of heat has occurred). Given this equation, an experiment is carried out both to measure actual skin and contact temperatures for a range of materials and surface temperatures, and to relate these objective values to people's subjective estimates of the comfort of the temperature. The results of the experiment (the observed values) are compared with the predictions given by the equation, and with values that have been suggested by a British Standard for surface temperatures. The results suggest that the predicted and observed values are in reasonable agreement, and that these values are less than those in the British Standard—that is, they are conservative in relation to it.

This study highlights two important methodological points. First, a mathematical model of human response, if accurate and reliable, can save a great deal of experimental effort. If the prediction equation for safe surface temperatures had been shown to be unreliable, then in the absence of other models it would be necessary to determine safe surface temperatures experimentally for each new material and application. This would be time consuming and expensive. Having established, however, that the model gives acceptable results, it can now be used by engineers and designers without recourse to more experimental studies. In other words, the model provides a general answer and not a specific one.

The second point is that ergonomics benefits by using information from other scientific disciplines. Although ergonomics is a human science, the human body can be described in physical terms and behaves according to the laws of physics. It is the physical information about the transfer of heat which allows a general solution to be derived; it would be difficult or impossible to do this solely on the basis of subjective reaction. In discussing heat transfer, the author makes use of differential calculus; the reader unfamiliar with this should not be dismayed, but bear in mind that the result is the useful information contained in equation 5.

See page 197 for the article, which is reproduced in full from *Applied Ergonomics*.

Example 3

L.A. Smith and J.L. Smith: Observations on in-house ergonomics training for first-line supervisors. 1984 *Applied Ergonomics*, volume 15, number 1, pp 11–14.

It has been said that if you ask one hundred people the meaning of the word 'ergonomics', 50 don't know, 45 think you mean economics, and 5 say it's to do with the design of seats. Any professional ergonomist will testify that one of the main problems met by the discipline is that of getting itself recognised. Only when this has happened will a significant ergonomics input be possible in the design of products, systems, workplaces, and work practices. Yet experience has shown us that, once the subject and its implications have been recognised, ergonomics often is incorporated enthusiastically into the design and evaluation process.

Knowledge of ergonomics, as with any other field of study, can take a number of levels, ranging from a basic understanding of the meaning of the term through to full-time professional involvement in the subject. Full-time professionals will have studied the subject, generally to first degree level and sometimes to higher degree level, and will have much practical experience on which to draw; but this is not to deny the value of a reasonable grasp of basic principles by someone whose main activities lie in engineering, design, management, production, or any other professional function. Such a person would be able to make a simple appraisal of the places in which he or she works, and the equipment used or the products made there, and would be able either to suggest modifications to these or, if the problem is too complex, to know that the advice of an ergonomics professional is called for. Straightforward ergonomics changes are probably more a reflection of a changed attitude about the equipment and facilities people use, rather than of an extensive technical knowledge.

In addition to formal degree courses in ergonomics at universities and colleges, short courses are frequently given to engineers, designers, and managers to develop this change in attitude and to instil the basic principles. These courses may be presented to employees in a single company, or may be 'open' and attended by people from a variety of companies. They may be concentrated into one or two days, or distributed over a number of weeks. They may involve a general introduction to ergonomics or may concentrate on certain aspects of the subject. All these choices are resolved according to the aim of the course and the nature of the participants.

The article reprinted here is an account of the development and evaluation of short courses for industrial supervisors in the USA. It argues the need for such courses, describes the structure of a typical course, and presents data pertaining to the evaluation of the course by those who had attended it. It concludes by demonstrating the value of these courses, and makes some suggestions for course design. Other experience in the UK has shown that many of the suggestions and points made in this article are applicable in many industries and countries.

See page 206 for the article, which is reproduced in full from *Applied Ergonomics*.

Example 4

E.T. Klemmer and D.J. Dooling: Making human factors effective in industry: examples from business telephone systems. 1983 *Applied Ergonomics*, volume 14, number 4, pp 279–283.

This paper describes the involvement of ergonomics in the various phases of the conception, design, development, and evaluation of a number of telephonic products. It identifies these phases, starting with customer studies to define new services, and finishing with the field evaluation of a marketed product, and gives some examples for each of the phases.

Example 4   161

The authors illustrate a number of important points in their article. First, they demonstrate that ergonomics can be used profitably in all the phases of the development of the product. Ergonomists frequently make a contribution in this way, rather than being involved in just one phase. Although the examples in the article relate to different products in the different phases, they show that a single product could be created with the help of ergonomics throughout its development and evaluation.

The second point is that as products become more complex and more flexible, the ergonomics problems in their design become more acute. A complex product must still be usable, and a flexible one must be able to carry out its functions in a variety of circumstances. The development of computer systems illustrates this issue well, and since computers are increasingly being used to control communications devices such as telephones, the same arguments apply. When the ergonomics problems in product design were limited to questions of physical size and shape, it could be said that solutions were relatively straightforward. Now that we are dealing, not only with size, shape, or force, but also with the processing of information and the making of decisions, the problems we have to solve are at the same time more difficult and more challenging. This is recognised by the authors when they argue that the design of operating procedures for business telephones is more important than the physical design.

The last point relates to the organisational role of the ergonomist in this type of business environment. In the section titled 'integrating human factors into system design', the authors give a number of general principles concerning the stage at which ergonomics is used, the sorts of decisions that are aided by the ergonomist, the relationship between the ergonomist and other members of the design and manufacturing team, and the provision of ergonomics facilities. These principles can with advantage be applied to a large number of design problems, both within the advanced technology field and outside it.

See page 213 for the article, which is reproduced in full from *Applied Ergonomics*.

Postural muscle strain as a causal factor in the development of musculo-skeletal illness

R. H. Westgaard† and A. Aarås*

† Institute of Work Physiology, Gydas vei 8, Oslo 3, Norway
* Standard Telefon & Kabelfabrik A/S, Østre Aker v.33, Oslo 5, Norway

Musculo-skeletal complaints account for 30% of time lost through sick leave. A study was made at a small manufacturing plant in Norway among workers subjected to static muscle load, with particular reference to the relationship between such illness and muscle strain due to working conditions. The paper covers old working standards and ergonomic improvements made in 1975. The results show an increase in musculo-skeletal illness with increased length of employment and increased age.

Introduction

Complaints originating in the musculo-skeletal system are one of the most common categories of illnesses in Norway today. A survey of 9000 patients, treated by general practitioners, showed that 20% of all patients suffered from a musculo-skeletal complaint, accounting for 30% of time lost through sick leave (Borchgrevink et al, 1980). It has been estimated that the cost of each day of production lost through sick leave is in the order of £100 to the company and the community at large (the value of lost production and sickness benefits), amounting to approximately £1 million per 1000 workers each year for this particular category of illnesses. Thus, both the economic and medical implications of musculo-skeletal illnesses are serious, and apparently of increasing importance relative to other illnesses.

It is likely that many of these complaints are caused or enhanced by excessive muscular load due to the need to adopt awkward postures at work. The main symptom of musculo-skeletal disorder is pain, and a correlation between posture and signs or symptoms of such disorders has been demonstrated (Luopajärvi et al, 1979; Maeda et al, 1980; Bjelle et al, 1981). The situation at a small manufacturing plant in Norway has allowed us to carry out a quantitative study regarding the occurrence of musculo-skeletal illnesses (i.e. sick leaves with a relevant medical diagnosis) among workers in work situations demanding static muscle work, and in particular the relationship between such illnesses and muscle strain due to working conditions.

In the early 1970s the workers at Standard Telefon and Kabelfabrik's plant in Kongsvinger, Norway, frequently registered musculo-skeletal complaints, and the factory had at the same time a high rate of sick leave. The sick leave was therefore attributed to musculo-skeletal illness and new work places were designed, which allowed the workers more flexibility in adopting a suitable work posture. Arm rests on the chairs supported elevated arms, and thereby reduced muscular load on the shoulders and arms. The design of the work places made it possible to alternate between a sitting and standing posture. The new work places were introduced early in 1975, and a significant reduction of sick leave followed.

This paper describes the old work situations at the plant and the ergonomic adaptations made in 1975. The occurrence of documented incidences of sick leave due to musculo-skeletal illness in the old work situations is analysed and compared with similar data from other, less strenuous work situations. Another paper (Westgaard and Aarås, 1984) considers evidence to determine whether the ergonomic adaptations of the workplace have had any effect in improving the health of the workers. Preliminary reports from this study have been published (Aarås and Westgaard, 1979; Westgaard and Aarås, 1982).

Methods

Epidemiology

The work duties of all workers employed at the factory since the start in 1967 were identified, and all sick leaves of more than three days' duration when a doctor's certificate is required (usually made out by general practitioners in the area), were registered. The medical diagnoses were then collected at the local health authorities, by special permission granted by the Department of Health and Social Security. The sick leaves were classified according to the type of diagnosis, and times away from work were calculated for musculo-skeletal illnesses and all other illnesses combined, in percent of possible time at work.

The most frequent musculo-skeletal diagnoses were myalgia, dorsalgia, brachialgia, tendinitis, lumbago and ischialgia. Rheumatic illnesses (arthritis), although of musculo-skeletal origin, were included among 'other illnesses' since muscle strain is not a primary cause of this illness.

Interviews concerning feelings of discomfort and pain while working

All workers employed in the autumn of 1979 were questioned about the intensity and location of pain on different parts of the body. A distinction was made between pain experienced in a 'past' situation (this was not related to a specific time period, but if ailments of variable intensity had been experienced, the *worst* chronic pain intensity was indicated) and the 'present' situation (a subjective evaluation of average pain intensity in the last year). Pain intensity was graded according to a scale of six steps. It was attempted to differentiate between somatic pain in muscles and tendons and other sources of pain, like migraine. A question of whether any change in pain intensity could be associated with a specific time period or any particular event was included at the end of the interview.

Only information relating to the situation before the ergonomic adaptations is included in this paper. Comparative results describing discomfort in the 'past' and 'present' situation are presented in a following paper (Westgaard and Aarås, 1984).

The factory

General

STK's factory in Kongsvinger was established in 1967 to produce parts for telephone exchanges. An average of 36 men and women were employed in production work at the factory in 1968, increasing to 137 in 1971 and reducing to 103 in 1974 (Table 1). During the last few years the factory has had a work force of about 100 (Westgaard and Aarås, 1984). From 1967 to January 1975 a total of 251 women and 69 men were employed in production work. Most of the men were employed in the production of cable forms (see below). During the time the factory has been in existence, a product development has taken place. The production was first based on the telephone exchange system 8B, followed by the internal communication system Minimat. Until 1974, cable making and the 8B system accounted for more than 90% of all production work; in 1974, 87%. In 1974 to 1976 the 8B system was to a large extent replaced by the 10C and 11B systems. The 8B system was

Table 1   Number of workers employed at the different work systems 1967 to 1974

Work system	Total 1967–1974	Calendar year							
		1967	1968	1969	1970	1971	1972	1973	1974
Cable making	170	10	15	20	25	25	25	25	25
8B	506	26	28	42	70	102	94	79	65
Minimat	48	—	—	—	8	10	10	10	10
11B	3	—	—	—	—	—	—	—	3
Total	727	36	43	62	103	137	129	114	103

discontinued in 1980. Twenty to thirty workers have been producing cable forms (cable making) each year from 1967 until January 1975.

The production workers had a piecework pay system until May 1976, when a fixed pay system with a collective productivity agreement was introduced. Flexible working hours were introduced in January 1977. The factory has had the same management and the same foremen from 1967 until 1983.

Cable making

The production of cable forms began in January 1967. By January 1975, 89 workers had been employed in this production (29 women and 60 men). Total production time 1967 to 1974 was 170 man-labour years. The work situation is illustrated in Figs 1 to 3. About 5% of the time is used to hammer nails into a wooden board according to a detailed instruction sheet. Then (about 45% of the production time) the worker lays thin insulated wire between the nails. Approximately 35% of the time is used to sew the wires together with strong plastic bands. The final 15% of

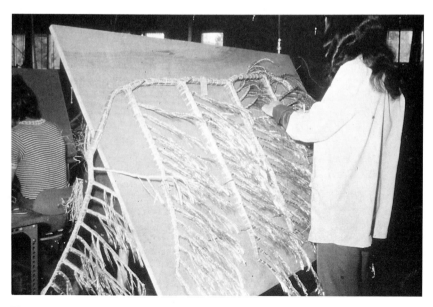

Figure 1   Cable making. The old workplace.

Figure 2   Cable making. The table is mounted on a hydraulic stand.

Figure 3   Cable making on a large table. Note improved low-luminance lighting introduced after 1980.

total production time is used to check the wiring and remove the cable from the table.

There are two sizes of wooden boards, 2 m × 1.5 m and 4 m × 1.5 m. The boards were mounted with fixed centre height before 1975, but the slope of the board could be altered in a stepwise manner. This mounting system did not allow any adjustment of the height of the work surface, to compensate for variations in the height of the workers and the cable forms. When working on large cable forms, the workers were forced to stretch considerably because of a large and too high working area.

Sewing of cable forms and laying of wires when working with the large forms were always done standing. It was possible to work seated when making small forms, but then the table top had to be angled almost horizontally to leave room for the feet underneath the lower edge of the table. This made the worker bend forward since the cable form was usually larger than the reaching area with a normal seated posture.

A new mounting system for the wooden board, based on a hydraulic cylinder, was introduced in the last half of 1975 (Fig. 2). This system allowed continuous adjustment of height and slope of the table. The large tables were made adjustable in the same way in 1977 (Fig. 3). Independent adjustment of height and slope of the table allowed each worker to find his own optimal work posture depending on his height and the size of the cable form, thereby reducing the strain on neck, shoulders and low back. Illumination was also improved, by replacing an angle-poise lamp fitted with a conventional tungsten bulb by neon tube lighting (in 1975).

The 8B system

Part production of the telephone exchange system 8B began in Kongsvinger in January 1967. By January 1975 231 persons had been employed with this production (222 women, 9 men) for a total of 506 man-labour years. The work system referred to as 8B in this paper is illustrated in Figs 4 to 6. About 10% of the work time is used to fasten the finished cable form to the metal frame, do other preparatory work and terminate the job. Otherwise, the work consists of connecting wires with bare ends to the needle shaped terminals on the metal frame. Before 1972 about 25% of the connections were made using tin soldering, and later about 10%. The rest is done by wrapping. (The wire is placed in a 'wrapping gun' which is then positioned on to the terminal. Thereafter the wrapping gun spins the wire around the terminal.) The metal frame is 100 cm wide and 40 to 80 cm high, depending on the number of horizontal 'rows' on the frame (usually 6 to 12). Working time along one row varies between $\frac{1}{2}$ and $1\frac{1}{2}$ h. The work is then immediately continued on the row above or below the finished row. It is necessary to see small objects about 5 cm into the frame, which means that the angle between the line of sight and the horizontal plane must be small.

Before 1975 the metal frame was placed on a table of fixed height (Figs 4 and 5). Work on the lower rows necessitated a forward bending posture in order to satisfy the vision requirement. Most workers preferred to keep a seated posture as long as possible. The chair was therefore adjusted upwards when the worker moved on to higher rows, until the thighs were pushed against the lower edge of the table surface.

The chair had a wooden seat and was described by many as hard and uncomfortable. A loose pillow was often used as seat padding. The chair had a wooden back support which was described as hard and badly shaped. The back support could be regulated forwards and backwards, but gave no support for the lumbar area of the back when bending forward. The chair had no arm rests. It was therefore not possible to support elevated arms while working on the middle rows, although the

Figure 4 The 8B system. Old, high sitting posture. The shoulders are lifted. Electric wrapping gun.

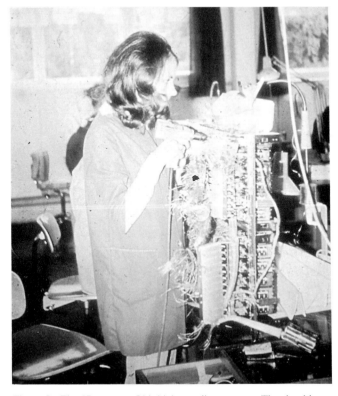

Figure 5 The 8B system. Old, high standing posture. The shoulders are lifted.

table acted as support when working on the lower two or three rows. The weight of the electric wrapping gun (about 1000 g) was not counterbalanced and this increased the static load on the muscles in the right shoulder and arm.

Work in the upper part of the frame had to be done standing (Fig. 5). Shoulders and arms were elevated, resulting in considerable static load on the shoulder and arm muscles.

Early in 1975 a new type of work place was introduced. The metal frame was placed on a hydraulic stand (Fig. 6) with a vertical movement of 60 cm, which was sufficient to allow both comfortable seated and standing postures. All seated work could be done at virtually the same height by adjusting the height of the frame. A lighter, air-propelled wrapping gun (350 g) with a counterbalancing system was also introduced.

In order to reduce static muscle load when working with elevated arms (necessary due to vision requirements) arm rests were mounted on an upholstered, padded chair (Fig. 7). The height and slope of the arm rests were adjustable and it was possible to turn them towards or away from the body. The left, curved arm rest gave the worker good support for an arm pointed towards a work area in front of the body. The arm rests were particularly effective in reducing static muscle load since the vertical working height at any time was no higher than the height of a horizontal row (5–10 cm).

With the new work place most of the work can be done seated using the arm rests, since the frame can be lowered all the way until the lower edge touches the thighs. When working on the upper rows a standing posture is still necessary. The frame would normally be positioned lower than with the old work place, but the need for good vision makes it still necessary to bend forward, elevate the arms and use an elbow angle of less than 90°. Static muscle load is nevertheless reduced also when standing due to a somewhat better working height and a lighter wrapping gun.

Figure 6 The 8B system. New work place. Air pressure wrapping gun. The headband is used to record head angle.

Figure 7   Chair with arm rests, introduced Spring 1975.

The original angle-poise lamp was replaced by a neon tube lamp, which gave a stronger and more even light over a larger area.

The Minimat system

The production of the Minimat internal communication system began in 1970. The production work is done on a large wooden board mounted on a hydraulic stand. The slope of the wooden board can be continuously adjusted, but is usually kept vertical. The height can be adjusted within a range of 60 cm (Fig. 8). Most of the work consists of wrapping wire ends to needle-shaped terminals as in the 8B system. The worker can work on one horizontal row after the other, keeping the working height to 5–10 cm.

When working on the lower part of the wooden board, the worker can adopt a well balanced sitting posture. When working on the middle rows, the board must be lowered to such an extent that there is no room for the legs below it, resulting in a forward bending, somewhat twisted posture in order to reach the work area. For approximately 15% of the total work time, it is necessary to stand in order to reach

Figure 8   The Minimat system. Sitting posture when working on the middle and lower rows. Note early arm rests on front chair.

the upper rows. The requirement for good vision is similar to that of the 8B system. The forearms are therefore lifted above elbow height resulting in static load of shoulder and arm muscles.

Until 1975 the same chair and wrapping gun as for the 8B system was used. In 1975 the new chair with arm rests and the lighter, counterbalanced wrapping gun described in the previous section was introduced. A neon light lamp was introduced, similar to that of the 8B system. Since 1975 there has been a continuous development of new products designed to improve the work situation. This has resulted in a new chair and a low-luminance lighting system which was introduced at Minimat, 10C and 11B after 1980 (shown in Fig. 12 for 11B).

The 10C system

Production of the 10C system began in 1974. The work object is a large metal frame, 236 cm × 60 cm, divided into seven to eight smaller 'sub-frames' which are mounted side by side along the length of the large frame (Figs 9 to 11). Most of the work (about 85%) consists of laying long wires between needle shaped terminals and connecting the wire ends to the terminals with a wrapping gun. Terminals which are joined together within a sub-frame (about 35% of total work time) are scattered over the whole working area, making the working height the same as the full height of the sub-frame (60 cm). This work is done seated (Fig. 9). Most wires join terminals in different sub-frames so that the wires cross several sub-frames or even the whole length of the large frame. This work (about 50% of total work time) is done standing (Fig. 10). The long working time (more than 100 h) has made it desirable for two workers to work together on the same frame.

Figure 9   The 10C system. Old, sitting posture.

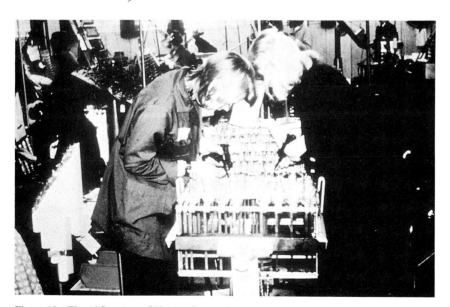

Figure 10   The 10C system. Old, standing posture.

At first the frame was placed in a stand which allowed step by step adjustment of the slope. It was also possible to adjust the height, but the whole frame had to be lifted by hand (weight 100 to 150 kg). Height adjustments of the frame were therefore never carried out in practice, but it was positioned midway between seated and standing posture. The seated posture caused static load of neck and back muscles due to forward bending since there was not room for the legs underneath the frame. The upper part of the area was above elbow height, resulting in static load on the shoulders and arm muscles.

For standing work, the frame was positioned horizontally. The working height was too low for some, resulting in a posture with neck and back bent forward. For others the working level was too high, making it necessary to lift shoulder and arms as well as bending the neck forward. Also, the wrapping gun was constructed for vertically mounted frames, so that the wrist had to be turned in the direction of the little finger when the frame was placed horizontally.

From the middle of 1975 the frame could be lowered or lifted to a suitable height, for both standing and seated work (Fig. 11). However, this did not reduce the working height when seated. Also, different body height of the two workers working together made it difficult to find an optimal adjustment when standing. It is therefore desirable that all work on a 10C frame is done by a single person, but lack of space has not allowed such an arrangement. Thus, the 10C system must still be considered strenuous.

Figure 11 The 10C system. Present work place with possibilities for regulating height and slope. Improved low-luminance lighting system.

The 11B system

The production of the 11B telephone exchange began in 1974 (Fig. 12). The frame is 78 cm by 100 cm and consists of two-four 'shelves' mounted on top of each other. About 75% of the work time is used to connect wire ends to terminals using a wrapping gun. Most connections are done within one shelf, while terminals in different shelves are connected in 20% of the work time. The rest of the time is used for sewing the wires together, fitting plugs and various other finishing work. The frame was mounted at a fixed height for a short period until spring 1975, when the frame was mounted on a hydraulic stand similar to the 8B frame. However, the large working height and the visual demands (as for the 8B system) meant that the workers had to keep the arms above elbow height to avoid bending the neck and back forward. Wrapping of wires between terminals in different shelves results in

Figure 12   The 11B system. Sitting posture when working on the lower rows of the frame. Note low-luminance lighting and new chair.

large working height and much bending and lifting of the body and arms even when the frame is in the most favourable position.

In 1975 the wrapping guns were counterbalanced and chairs with armrests introduced. Most workers use the armrests only when the work area is restricted to one of the two lower shelves. Then they have a seated working posture with limited working height, comfortable height of the frame and leg room underneath the frame. All other work is usually done standing to avoid a forward bending, seated posture. Neon lights have been used since 1976, until 1980, when low-luminance lighting was introduced. A new chair was also introduced in 1980.

Results

Total sick leave at STK, Kongsvinger, for the period 1967 to 1974 was 11.2%, which is similar to the average sick leave of female industrial workers in Norway in the same time period (11.5%, Conference of Employees statistics). Also, the grouping of sick leave in the long term (duration more than 3 days, a doctor's certificate is required) and short term sick leave is similar to that of the industry as a whole (9.9% at STK, Kongsvinger vs an industrial average of 10.3% for long term sick leave, 1.3% vs 1.2% for short term sick leave). However, there are two factors which suggest that sick leave at STK, Kongsvinger, even so, has been unusually high. Firstly, the workers at STK, Kongsvinger, were young (usually less than 25 years) and it is well known that long term sick leave in general is much reduced for this age group. Secondly, long term sick leave has not been uniform in this time period, but was low in the years 1967 to 1969 and then showed a substantial increase from 1970 to 1974, when it reached 16.9% of possible working time that year (Table 2). In contrast, short term sick leave remained at the same level throughout this period. Sick leave due to musculo-skeletal illnesses accounted for 5.3% of production time lost over the whole period, or more than half the total long term sick leave. The development of musculo-skeletal sick leave followed the same trend as total sick leave: low the first three years, then increasing rapidly during the years 1970 to 1974, reaching 10.0% of possible working time in 1974.

Table 2   Sick leave and turn-over at STK, Kongsvinger, in percent of possible working time (sick leave) or average number of people employed (turn-over)

	1967–1974	1967	1968	1969	1970	1971	1972	1973	1974
Short term sick leave (%)	1.3	1.5	1.1	1.3	1.6	1.3	1.1	1.4	1.3
Long term sick leave (%)	9.9	6.2	6.6	4.0	7.6	8.3	9.8	13.4	16.9
Musculo-skeletal sick leave (%)	5.3*	2.2	0.7	0.8	4.8	3.3	5.9	6.8	10.0
Turn-over (%)	30.1	2.8	25.6	27.4	41.7	35.0	36.4	27.2	20.4

* Includes time away from work in 1975 due to musculo-skeletal sick leaves starting in 1974

Turn-over of production workers is another interesting parameter since high turn-over also may indicate problems at work. Overall turn-over for the period 1967 to 1974 was high, 30.1% of the work force.

Thus, the rate of both sick leave and turn-over could be interpreted to indicate that the workers had considerable problems, and that these problems were of musculo-skeletal origin. This was also generally accepted by the management at the factory by the end of 1974. The likely cause of these problems was static muscle load in the shoulder and neck region (Westgaard and Aarås, 1984). Further analysis of the epidemiological data is therefore best done by considering the different work systems separately, since the work load varies from system to system. In particular, cable making specified a much more dynamic work situation than the other systems.

Table 3 shows musculo-skeletal sick leave, number of musculo-skeletal diagnoses and number of workers absent from work due to musculo-skeletal illness for the 8B system and cable making. Musculo-skeletal sick leave at the 8B system was 5.1% for the period 1967 to 1974. The sick leave at 8B each year did not differ much from that of the factory as a whole, which follows from the fact that 8B was by far the largest work system. Of the order of 20 workers were absent with musculo-skeletal illness each year in the years 1970 to 1974. Some workers had repeated sick leaves of this kind from year to year, making the total number of workers with musculo-skeletal sick leave at the 8B system 83. This is 35.9% of all workers employed at this system at any time until 1 January, 1975.

Table 3   Sick leave statistics of the 8B system and cable making

	8B								
	1967–1974	*1967*	*1968*	*1969*	*1970*	*1971*	*1972*	*1973*	*1974*
Musculo-skeletal sick leave (%)	5.1*	3.0	0.9	1.0	4.8	2.9	6.0	6.9	9.1
No of m-s diagnoses	124 (24.5%)	5	1	3	25	19	24	24	23
No of workers ill with m-s sick leave	83 (35.9%)	4	1	3	21	17	21	21	20

	Cable making								
	1967–1974	*1967*	*1968*	*1969*	*1970*	*1971*	*1972*	*1973*	*1974*
Musculo-skeletal sick leave (%)	4.7	0.2	0.3	0.4	4.1	3.8	2.8	6.1	11.9
No of m-s diagnoses	52 (30.6%)	1	1	4	6	8	12	12	8
No of workers ill with m-s sick leave	30 (33.7%)	1	1	4	6	6	8	7	7

* Includes time away from work in 1975 due to musculo-skeletal sick leaves starting 1974

Any difference in number of m-s diagnoses and number of workers with m-s sick leave is due to workers having more than one musculo-skeletal sick leave the same calendar year

The percentage shown for number of m-s diagnoses indicates number of m-s diagnoses as a fraction of man-labour years at 8B and cable making, respectively

Musculo-skeletal sick leave at cable making was 4.7% in the period 1967 to 1974. Workers at this system showed considerable variation in musculo-skeletal sick leave from year to year (2.8% in 1972, 11.9% in 1974), presumably due to the long duration of some sick leaves, combined with the low number of workers employed at this system. A total of 30 workers (33.7% of all workers employed at cable making by 1 January 1975) have been ill due to musculo-skeletal illness.

The durations of the musculo-skeletal sick leaves are shown in Fig. 13. Most sick leaves at the 8B system have a duration of 31 to 60 illness benefit days, and there

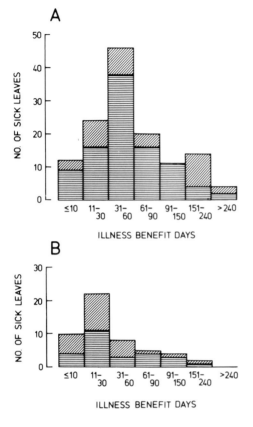

Figure 13   Duration of sick leaves due to musculo-skeletal illness at the 8B system (A) and cable making (B) for the period 1967 to 1974. The duration is measured in 'illness benefit' days (6 illness benefit days in a week). Sick leaves due to a complaint located in the neck, shoulders or arms are indicated by horizontal hatching, low back complaints by diagonal hatching.

are several cases of sick leave of more than half a year's duration. The individual episodes of musculo-skeletal illness must therefore be considered serious in terms of the workers' health. It is also clear that a majority of the complaints are localised to the shoulder and neck region (75% *vs* 25% low back diagnoses). The sick leaves were of shorter duration at cable making, most commonly 11 to 30 illness benefit days. Thus, the episodes of musculo-skeletal illness, although frequent also at cable making, have on average been less serious at this system than at the 8B system. Also, there is a difference in the localisation of the illnesses, with 49% low back diagnoses at cable making. The difference in duration of sick leaves is statistically significant by a chi-square test both when all musculo-skeletal sick leaves are included (p<0.001) and when only neck, shoulder, and arm-diagnoses are considered (p<0.01).

Musculo-skeletal sick leave of different age groups of workers at the 8B system in the years 1970–1974 is shown in Fig. 14 together with all long term sick leave of different age groups of women with administrative and clerical work in the Norwegian telecommunication system, and of domestic assistants in the same company. Musculo-skeletal sick leave at the 8B system is about twice as high as total

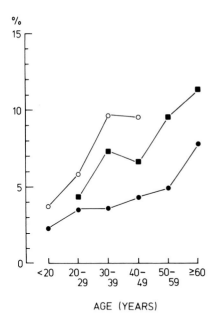

%

AGE (YEARS)

Figure 14   Sick leave for different age groups, measured in percent of possible working time. Musculo-skeletal sick leave at the 8B system (open circles) is compared with total long-term sick leave of domestic assistants (filled squares) and women with administrative and clerical work (filled circles) in the Norwegian Telecommunication system (1976 statistics).

long-term sick leave for female workers of the same age doing general office work, and also higher than total long-term sick leave of female workers in a manual work situation generally considered strenuous. As musculo-skeletal sick leave amounts to about half the total sick leave of workers at the 8B system, it is clear that sick leave for this system was very high in the 5 years preceding the ergonomic adaptations, when the age of the workers is taken into account.

The sick leave statistics of STK's Kongsvinger plant have shown that the workers suffered a high rate of illness, primarily due to musculo-skeletal disorders. This is not by itself sufficient evidence to claim that conditions at work are detrimental to the health of the workers. However, if there is a causal relationship between strain at work and musculo-skeletal sick leave, one would expect that workers with long periods of employment are more likely to have experienced musculo-skeletal illness than workers recently employed. Also, the time from employment until their first musculo-skeletal sick leave could be a possible indication of strain in a work situation, if this time period is of the same length for most workers with such illness.

In Fig. 15 time of employment of all workers working with the 8B system before 1974 is shown. Due to high turnover, the largest group of workers was employed less than 1 year and the second largest between 1 and 2 years. Nevertheless, 31 workers were still employed at the factory by 1980, ie, had been working at the 8B system for at least 6 years. The hatched part of each column shows how many within the different groups have been absent from work due to musculo-skeletal sick leave. Fig. 15C (triangles) indicates the fraction of workers at the 8B system with musculo-skeletal sick leave, as a function of time of employment. The fraction increases rapidly with time of employment: it is already 39% among those employed between 1 and 2 years and is about 70% for those employed more than 2 years. This is in contrast to Fig. 15B which shows similar data for a group of 92

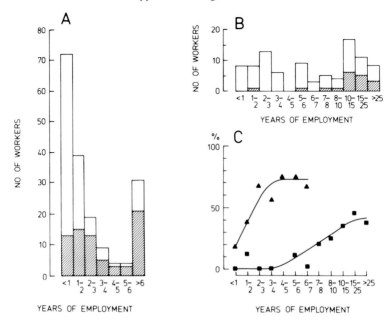

Figure 15   A. The histogram indicates time of employment for all workers employed at the 8B system before 1974 by January 1980. The hatched part of each column shows how many within each group have experienced one or several sick leaves due to musculo-skeletal illness. B. Similar data for a control group of women with administrative and clerical work. C. Percent of workers at the 8B system (filled triangles) and with administrative/clerical work (filled squares) with musculo-skeletal sick leaves as a function of years of employment. The data in C are derived from A and B by dividing number of workers with musculo-skeletal sick leave by total number of workers within each group.

women with general office work, and where only 1 of 35 workers employed for less than 5 years has suffered a musculo-skeletal illness resulting in a sick leave. The ratio of workers with musculo-skeletal sick leave in this group is shown in Fig. 15C (filled squares). There is a moderate increase in this ratio with long periods of employment, averaging about 40% for those employed 10 years or longer.

Fig. 16 shows time of employment until first musculo-skeletal sick leave for those having suffered such an illness. Workers at the 8B work system most frequently had their first episode within the first year of employment (16A), while workers at cable making most frequently suffered their first musculo-skeletal illness 1 to 2 years after employment (16B). This is particularly so if only women are considered. There is no clear grouping of time to first musculo-skeletal sick leave among the women with general office work, and certainly no tendency for such sick leaves to happen within the first two years after work (Fig. 16C). Fig. 17 shows time to first musculo-skeletal sick leave as a function of age for each individual case. It is clear that many of those working at the 8B system became ill due to musculo-skeletal complaints as early as 3 to 6 months after employment. Also, a majority of those who became ill were younger than 20 years when employed. There is no obvious effect of age for workers at the 8B system from the below 20 year to the 20 to 30 year and the 30 to 40 year age groups with respect to this parameter. Similarly, the same fraction of workers employed became ill in the below 20 group (40%) as in the 30 to 40 year group (41%). The main cause of the major increase in working days lost due to musculo-skeletal sick leave from the less than 20 year to the 30 to 40 year group

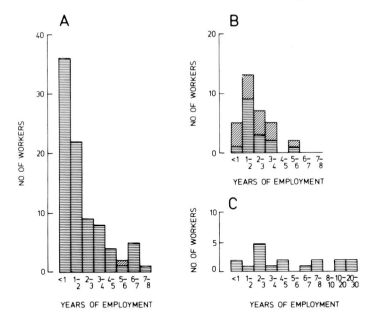

Figure 16   Time from employment to first musculo-skeletal sick leave for workers at the 8B system (A), cable making (B) and with administrative/clerical work (C). Horizontal hatching indicates female workers, diagonal hatching men.

(Fig. 14) is therefore that there was a tendency to longer duration of sick leaves with increasing age.

In order to further evaluate the symptoms of musculo-skeletal illness, the workers employed at the factory in the autumn of 1978 (97 men and women) were questioned regarding intensity and location of discomfort/pain while working. The intensity was indicated according to a scale from 0 to 5 (none, very little, little, some, considerable, very much). Fifty-six of the 97 workers had experienced a sick leave due to musculo-skeletal illness. Fifty-two of the 56 workers with such sick leaves indicated 3, 4 or 5 as the maximum level of discomfort (regardless of location on the body, Fig. 18A). This range may in part be due to genuine differences in the intensity of pain experienced, and in part due to differences in the perception of the discomfort. However, since pain is the major symptom of musculo-skeletal disorder, the levels 3, 4 and 5 apparently indicate substantial complaints of this kind. Among the 41 workers who had not experienced musculo-skeletal illness, 23 (56%) stated that they had experienced pain at level 3 or 4 (Fig. 18B). The age and sex distributions of the two groups were similar, as was the period of employment. One would therefore not expect any systematic variation in pain indication from one group to the other. Thus, 75 of 97 workers can be said to have suffered a significant musculo-skeletal symptom (level 3, 4 or 5) at work, by this reasoning.

Fig. 19 shows the percentage of workers having experienced a complaint of intensity 3, 4 or 5 at different parts of the body while working at the 8B system (open circles) or cable making (filled circles). Only those employed before 1974 are included, ie, with at least one year's experience of the old work situation. Complaints located to the head and neck have been much more frequent among workers at the 8B system than at cable making. Shoulder complaints have been frequent among both groups while complaints in the low back region have been relatively infrequent among workers at the 8B system, and more frequent among workers at

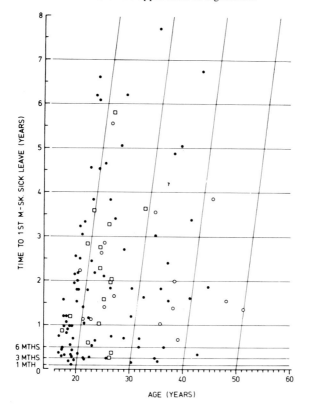

Figure 17   Time from employment to first musculo-skeletal sick leave as a function of age for workers at the 8B system (filled symbols) and cable making (open symbols). Open and filled circles indicate women at cable making and 8B, open squares men at cable making. Diagonal lines show age development when age at employment is 20, 30, 40 or 50 years.

cable making. There have been few complaints located to the lower part of the body.

The location of complaints on the basis of the interviews is in good agreement with the body location of the musculo-skeletal diagnoses and the likely location of the muscle load. Muscles in the neck and shoulders must be under considerable strain with work postures as illustrated in Figs 4 and 5. Also, it is well known that neck tension may provoke tension headache. One would also expect fewer complaints in the low back region for workers at the 8B system due to the upright sitting or standing posture. In contrast, workers at cable making, with their forward bending posture and elevated arms, can be expected to develop complaints in the shoulders and the low back region.

Discussion

The object of this paper has been to present evidence which allows a quantitative evaluation of a possible relationship between adverse working conditions and the

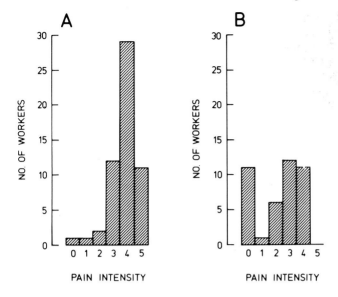

Figure 18 Highest indication of discomfort/pain, regardless of location on body, by workers with (A) or without (B) sick leave due to musculo-skeletal disorders.

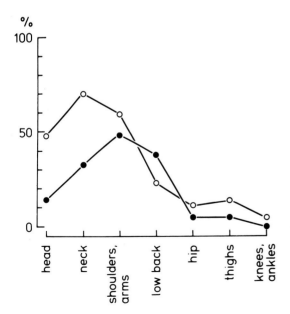

Figure 19 Percent of workers at the 8B system (open circles) and cable making (filled circles) with a significant musculo-skeletal symptom (i.e., a painful experience of intensity 3, 4 or 5 while working) at different locations on the body.

development of disorders in the musculo-skeletal system. This evidence may be summarised as follows:

• The work situations (in particular the 8B system) at STK's Kongsvinger factory in the years 1967 to 1974 imposed continuous muscle strain on specific muscles in the shoulder and neck region.
• There was a high rate of sick leave due to musculo-skeletal illnesses among the workers in these work situations (mostly young women). Sick leave due to these illnesses was low the first few years, thereafter increasing rapidly to a maximum of 10.0% in 1974.
• When comparing sick leave between workers of the same age, it was found that sick leave due to musculo-skeletal illnesses for workers in one of the work situations at STK, Kongsvinger, (the 8B system) was higher than total long-term sick leave for another group of workers with a generally strenuous occupation (domestic assistants), and much higher than total long-term sick leave among women with general office work.
• The occurrence of musculo-skeletal sick leave was much more frequent among those having been employed for more than 2 years (70%) than among those employed for shorter periods of time (the 8B system). Even so, 40% of those employed between 1 and 2 years had already experienced a prolonged sick leave of this kind. There was also a high rate of labour turn-over. In contrast, only one of 35 women with general office work and employed less than 5 years had suffered a similar kind of illness resulting in a sick leave.
• Workers at the 8B system most commonly had their first sick leave due to musculo-skeletal illness within the first year after employment, much earlier than workers at cable making. This category of sick leaves was of much longer duration at the 8B system than at cable making. There was no tendency for musculo-skeletal sick leaves to occur soon after employment within the control group of female workers with general office work.
• Symptoms of musculo-skeletal complaints have been very common among workers at the 8B system and cable making. The location on the body of the symptoms was in good agreement with the distribution of the medical diagnoses.

There is no doubt that there has been an unusually high rate of musculo-skeletal illness among the workers at STK, Kongsvinger, in general, and the 8B system in particular. It is also clear that the work situations have been strenuous, with the strain mainly affecting a limited number of muscles in the shoulder and neck region when working at the 8B system. However, musculo-skeletal illness may also develop as a result of other factors than work load, for instance as a complication because of other illnesses, due to general defects of the musculo-skeletal system, due to muscle spasms as a consequence of problems of a psychological nature, or to strenuous leisure time activities. Thus, one should not conclude that the work situation is the major causal factor for any individual case of musculo-skeletal disorder. However, it is very unlikely that those employed at the 8B system have a sufficiently different life situation to other women of the same age to explain the group differences in sick leave due to musculo-skeletal disorders. The work load and, specifically, the strain on shoulder and neck muscles, must therefore be considered a major causal factor in the development of musculo-skeletal disorders among workers at STK, Kongsvinger, and the 8B system in particular.

In this analysis, musculo-skeletal sick leave has been used as an indicator of musculo-skeletal disorders. This indicator implies that someone has made an appointment to see a doctor, usually because of symptoms of pain, and the doctor, following a medical examination, has agreed that the condition is sufficiently serious to make the patient unable to work. This is not necessarily the best indicator of a pathophysiological condition of the musculo-skeletal system, since many other factors may influence the decision to see a doctor. It is well known that sick leave varies considerably from country to country, and is particularly high in the Scandinavian countries. Ignoring for the moment any differences in the statistical basis, such differences could be due to the welfare system in these countries which ensures very high job safety and no economic loss when someone is absent from work due to illness. This does not imply that the sick leaves were inappropriate. On the contrary, the interviews showed that many had suffered long periods with intense pain prior to sick leave, and that many in fact did not see a doctor despite considerable problems of this kind. Gross differences in rate of sick leave between countries could therefore be due to alternative strategies in trying to cope with ailments. If muscle soreness or pain becomes a problem, the worker may choose to terminate the job, use pain-killing drugs, receive physiotherapy outside working hours, or simply try to tolerate a high level of pain, rather than accept a sick leave. Alternatively, there may be subtle differences in the opportunity to avoid muscle load in apparently similar work situations (differences in frequency of rest pauses, less work load, possibilities of job rotation, etc), but we feel that such factors are unlikely to be grossly different from one industrialised country to another. We therefore suggest that the social system of the Scandinavian countries contributes to making the rate of sick leave due to musculo-skeletal illness a sensitive indicator of underlying musculo-skeletal symptoms which is common to workers in similar, constrained work situations throughout the industrialised countries (Partridge et al, 1965; Ferguson, 1971; Maeda, 1977; Kuorinka and Koskinen, 1979; Maeda et al, 1980; Westerling and Jonsson, 1980).

Acknowledgements

We are grateful to Dr O. Midttun for providing the material for statistical analysis of our control population of women with general office work.

References

AARÅS, A., and WESTGAARD, R.H. (1979). *Ergonomics*, **22**, 729. Evidence of reduced illness among factory workers as a result of individually chosen working positions

BJELLE, A., HAGBERG, M., and MICHAELSSON, G. (1981). *Br J Indust Med*, **38**, 356–363. Occupational and individual factors in acute shoulder-neck disorders among industrial workers

BORCHGREVINK, C.F., BREKKE, T.H., and ØGAR, B. (1980). *Tidskr Nor Lægeforen*, **100**, 439–445. Musculo-skeletal illness in general practice (In Norwegian)

FERGUSON, D. (1971). *Br J Indust Med*, **28**, 280–285. An Australian study of telegraphists' cramp

KUORINKA, I., and KOSKINEN, P. (1979). *Scand J Work Environ & Health*, **5**: Suppl 3, 39–47. Occupational rheumatic diseases and upper limb strain in manual jobs in a light mechanical industry

LUOPAJÄRVI, T., KUORINKA, I., VIROLAINEN, M., and HOLMBERG, M. (1979). *Scand J Work Environ & Health*, **5**: Suppl 3, 48–55. Prevalence of tenosynovitis and other injuries of the upper extremities in repetitive work

MAEDA, K. (1977). *J. Human Ergology*, **6**, 193–202. Occupational cervicobrachial disorder and its causative factors

MAEDA, K., HÜNTING, W., and GRANDJEAN, E. (1980). *J Occup Med*, **22**, 810–816. Localised fatigue in accounting-machine operators

PARTRIDGE, R.E.H., ANDERSON, J.A.D., MCCARTHY, M.A., and DUTHIE, J.J.R. (1965). *Ann Rheum Dis*, **24**, 332–340. Rheumatism in light industry

RUD, J. (1975). *Tidskr Nor Lægeforen*, **95**, 1661–1664. Adult disabled (In Norwegian)

WESTERLING, D., and JONSSON, B. G. (1980). *Scand J Soc Med*, **8**, 131–136. Pain from the neck-shoulder region and sick leave

WESTGAARD, R.H., and AARÅS, A. (1982). *Ergonomics*, **25**, 339–340. Inter-departmental education and co-operation may enable medium-sized companies to solve their own ergonomics problems

WESTGAARD, R.H., and AARÅS, A. (1984). *Appl Ergonomics*, in preparation. The effect of improved workplace design on the development of work-related musculo-skeletal illness

The effect of improved workplace design on the development of work-related musculo-skeletal illnesses

R. H. Westgaard† and A. Aarås*

† Institute of Work Physiology, Gydas vei 8, Oslo 3, Norway
* Standard Telefon og Kabelfabrik A/S, Østre Aker v. 33, Oslo 5, Norway

An earlier paper (Westgaard and Aarås, 1984) described the work environ-ment and the health situation of production workers at a small Norwegian factory, prior to an extensive ergonomics effort which primarily aimed to reduce static muscle strain by constructing new workplaces. It was con-cluded that the old work situation significantly contributed to a high level of musculo-skeletal disorders, most likely because the old work situation made it necessary to work with a high level of muscle load for long periods of the working day. This second paper concerns the other important query which initiated this study: Have the extensive ergonomics and environmen-tal efforts at this factory had any effect in terms of improved health of the workers? The factory, the old workplaces and the ergonomics adaptations were described in the preceding paper, and are therefore not included here.

Methods

The epidemiological methods and material are similar to those of the preceding paper. In addition, electromyographic recordings of muscle load on the upper and lower trapezius muscle while working on the 8B system are presented in this paper. The recordings were obtained by surface electrodes of our own construction with two electrodes and a preamplifier integrated in one recording unit. The electrodes are circular with a diameter of 6 mm and a centre distance of 20 mm. The signals were stored by using an Oxford Medilog portable tape recorder, and later analysed by using a Nord-10 computer with a specially developed on-line program. The analysis is based on numeric integration of the rectified EMG signal over 2 s intervals, resulting in discrete values which are a measure of average electrical activity of the muscle in this interval. These values, as a fraction of the values at maximal voluntary contraction, were used as a measure of muscle force. This is a true measure of muscle force only if the relationship between integrated electrical activity and muscle force is a linear one. While this may be so for some muscles (Bigland and Lippold, 1954), there are many examples of a non-linear relationship of this kind (Lindström *et al*, 1974; Komi and Viitasalo, 1976; Chaffin *et al*, 1980), and it is therefore necessary to calibrate force and EMG activity at varying levels of muscle force to be able to predict accurately the absolute level of force. However, a linear relationship between force and integrated EMG activity is usually a good approximation at the low levels of force present in these work situations. Thus, the estimates of muscle force based on the EMG recordings are uncertain in terms of the absolute level of load since there was no force-EMG calibration, but a reduction of the integrated EMG signal of 50% from one work situation to another can be interpreted to signify the same relative reduction in muscle force.

Results

Table 1 shows the number of production workers at the different systems from 1975 until the end of 1982. In this period the employment at cable making and Minimat remained stable, the 8B system was terminated at the Kongsvinger factory, the 11B system fell back to a low level after a few years with relatively high employment, while the 10C system has shown a steady increase until 1982. Total production time for each of these systems has been between 97 and 244 man-labour years.

Table 1   Number of workers employed at the different work systems 1975–1982

Work system	Total 1975–1982	Calendar year							
		1975	*1976*	*1977*	*1978*	*1979*	*1980*	*1981*	*1982*
Cable making	244	30	30	30	23	31	30	30	40
8B	97	35	20	20	9	11	2	0	0
Minimat	140	10	10	10	14	20	20	16	40
10C	222	14	14	18	24	22	46	56	28
11B	123	12	20	20	22	11	19	13	6
Total	941	101	94	98	92	95	117	115	114

The effect of ergonomic adaptations in muscle strain

The main purpose of the ergonomics adaptations was to reduce strain on specific muscles in the shoulders and neck region. The effect was assessed by electromyographic recordings from the relevant muscles while working at the 8B system. Figs 1 and 2 give examples of the results. Fig. 1A shows a 51 min recording from the upper right trapezius muscle while the worker has been working along the same row (8th row, high sitting posture) on the frame of the 8B system. Each point indicates average muscular activity of a 2 s interval in percent of activity at maximal voluntary contraction, as described in "Methods". The worker finished the left half of the row first, using the old workplace. There was a pause while the frame was moved to the new workplace and work continued on the right half of the same row adopting the new posture. There was static contraction of the upper right trapezius muscle throughout the experiment (no 2 s periods near zero), but the median value was reduced from 25% in the old work situation to 13% in the new one. Thus the muscle load was substantially higher in both work situations than is considered acceptable (Bjørksten and Jonsson, 1977). The ergonomics adaptations have nevertheless reduced the load on the upper trapezius muscle by half when working in this row.

Fig. 1B shows a similar recording from upper right trapezius when working on the 11th row (standing posture). In this experiment, work began with the new posture. There was a pause while working with the new posture and a new pause while the frame was moved to the old workplace. The muscle strain was less than on the 8th row for this person, but even so the load significantly increased as the worker moved from the new to the old workplace.

Fig. 2 shows EMG recordings from a whole working day. The recording lasted 5 h 35 min, divided into four recording periods of 1 h 43 min, 1 h 51 min, 1 h 31 min

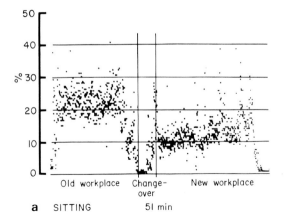

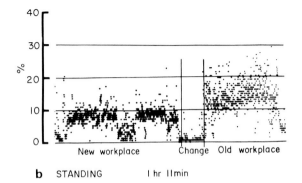

Figure 1 Muscle load on upper right trapezius muscle based on EMG recordings (in % of EMG activity at maximal contraction). A. Old, high sitting posture, then new posture. B. New, then old standing posture.

and 30 min. The results are presented in the same way as in Fig. 1, and recordings from upper right and lower right trapezius are shown. This working day was divided into three parts. In the first of these and in the first part of the second recording period, insulation was removed from the wire ends and the frame was prepared for the wrapping work. Wrapping was then done on the left half of the frame from first to tenth row in the new work situation. Finally, the same work was done on the right half of the frame, using the old workplace.

There was a low level of muscle load most of the time during the preparatory work, but the load on the upper trapezius increased in the last half of the first recording period and was high and very variable in the first part of the second period. This was when the cable form was fastened to the frame. When wrapping of wire ends to the terminals started (▼), the muscle activity became less variable, ie, the muscle contraction was more static. The muscle activity was interrupted by a short pause soon after the wrapping started and by lunch, as indicated on the figure. Work on the upper rows continued after lunch (first part of third recording period) and the muscle activity was now reduced, compared with the lower rows (before lunch). This is probably due to the lowering of the frame and the standing posture of the worker which allows further relaxation of the shoulder muscles.

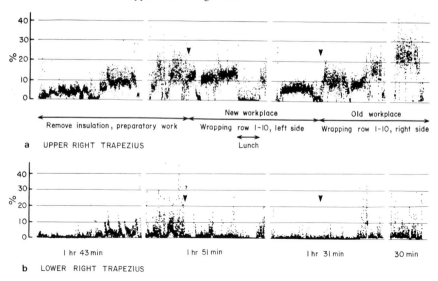

Figure 2 Muscle load (in % of EMG activity at maximal contraction) on upper and lower right trapezius muscles throughout a working day consisting of preparatory work, then wrapping wire ends using the old workplace and finally the new workplace. Further details in the text.

The level of activity with the old posture (▼) was similar to that with the new posture when working on the lower rows, but this time the muscle load increased with increased working height up to a mean level of about 25% on the upper rows (fourth recording period). In comparison, the mean level of muscle activity in the new work situation was never higher than 12–14%. Normally it would be necessary to work with high load on the upper trapezius for about 2 h each day. The ergonomics adaptations of the 8B workplace — if the results presented here are typical — have reduced the load on specific muscles by half throughout a significant period of the working day, but the load is probably still higher than considered acceptable.

Sick leave statistics

Long term sick leave was relatively stable in the years 1975 to 1982, averaging 9.4% of possible working time for the whole period (Table 2). This is similar to average sick leave in the period 1967 to 1974, but in this first period long-term sick leave showed a steep increase to 13.4% in 1973 and to 16.9% in 1974. Fig. 3 illustrates the development of long-term sick leave from 1967 to 1982. The sharp interruption of the upward trend in 1975 coincided with the implementation of the ergonomics adaptations. The hatched part of the columns in Fig. 3 indicates sick leave due to musculo-skeletal complaints (also shown in Table 2). The development of musculo-skeletal sick leave mirrors the development of total long-term sick leave, but with some variation from year to year which must be expected on account of the occasional very long sick leave and the relatively low number of production workers. Average musculo-skeletal sick leave in the years 1975 to 1982 was 3.1% of total production time, while it was 5.3% in the period 1967 to 1974 (Table 2). This reduction is statistically significant (p<0.01), and even more dramatic when compared with the two years immediately preceding the ergonomics adaptations

Table 2   Sick leave and turn-over at STK Kongsvinger in percent of possible working time/ average number of people employed

	1967–1974	1975–1982	1975	1976	1977	1978	1979	1980	1981	1982
Short term sick leave (%)	1.3	1.5	1.5	1.7	1.8	1.8	1.7	1.2	1.3	1.2
Long term sick leave (%)	9.9	9.4	10.0	9.3	7.9	8.8	10.6	10.6	9.8	8.5
Musculo-skeletal sick leave (%)	5.3	3.1	5.5 (2.9*)	2.3	4.3	5.0	3.1	2.6	2.4	2.9
Turn-over (%)	30.1	7.6	21.8	6.4	4.1	6.5	4.2	7.7	8.7	1.7

* Excludes sick leave in 1975 from musculo-skeletal sick leaves starting in 1974.

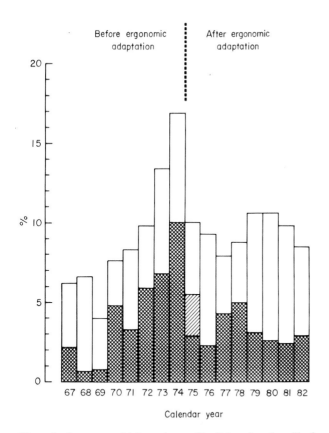

Figure 3   Long term sick leave (more than 3 days duration, % of possible working time each year) at STK, Kongsvinger in the years 1967 to 1982. The hatched parts of the columns indicate long term sick leave due to musculo-skeletal illness. Single hatching in 1975 indicates musculo-skeletal sick leave beginning in 1974.

(6.8 and 10.0%). In contrast, musculo-skeletal sick leave in 1975 was 5.5%, or 2.9% if sick leave beginning in 1974 is excluded.

Simultaneously with the reduction in long-term sick leave there has been a statistically significant (p<0.001) reduction in labour turn-over (Table 2). Turn-over in the years 1975 to 1982 was 7.6% of total man-labour years (i.e. average number of workers), while it was 30.1% in the period 1967 to 1974. Fig. 4 shows the development of labour turn-over from 1967 to 1982. In contrast to long-term sick leave and labour turn-over, short-term sick leave has remained stable (Table 2).

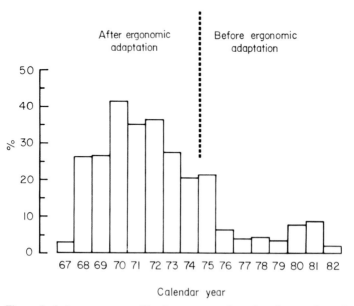

Figure 4 Labour turn-over (% of average number of workers each year) at STK, Kongsvinger in the years 1967 to 1982.

These results indicate a clear positive effect of the ergonomics adaptations in terms of improved health and job acceptability among the workers. However, the changes in the production programme resulted in new work situations for many of the workers, independent of the ergonomics adaptations. In order to assess the effect of the adaptations as such, it is necessary to compare sick leave statistics of workers with the same work task before and after their introduction. This is only possible for cable making and the 8B system where there has been a reasonable production volume both with the old and the new work situations.

Table 3 gives the results. Musculo-skeletal sick leave at cable making was reduced by two thirds, from 4.7% in the period 1967 to 1974 to 1.6% in the period 1975 to 1982. The number of sick leaves with musculo-skeletal diagnoses was also significantly reduced from 30.6% of total man-labour years in 1967–1974 to 14.3% of total man-labour years in 1975–1982. Thus, there has been a clear and statistically significant reduction in sick leave due to musculo-skeletal illnesses of workers employed only at cable making.

The situation is less clear at the 8B system. Musculo-skeletal sick leave for the period 1975 to 1981 (4.6%) was not much reduced compared with the period 1967 to 1974 (5.1%). However, it was reduced relative to musculo-skeletal sick leave in 1973 and 1974 (6.9 and 9.1%), immediately preceding the ergonomics adaptations. Also, the number of sick leaves due to musculo-skeletal diagnoses in percentage of

Table 3   Sick leave statistics of the 8B system and cable making

	8B									
	1967–1974	1975–1980	1975	1976	1977	1978	1979	1980	1981	1982
Musculo-skeletal sick leave (%)	5.1	4.6*	5.1	4.4	7.4	10.4	1.7	25.4	—	—
No of m-s diagnoses	124 (24.5%)	16 (16.5%)	4	2	4	4	2	0	—	—
No of workers ill with m-s sick leave	83 (35.9%)	11 (33.3%)	4	2	2	4	4	2	0	—

	Cable making									
	1967–1974†	1975–1982	1975	1976	1977	1978	1979	1980	1981	1982
Musculo-skeletal sick leave (%)	4.7	1.6*	5.7 (3.3*)	0.4	1.6	1.2	0.9	0.4	1.7	2.7
No of m-s diagnoses	52 (30.6%)	35 (14.3%)	6	2	5	5	5	0	2	10
No of workers ill with m-s sick leave	30 (33.7%)	14 (42.4%)	5	2	5	5	5	0	2	9

* Excludes sick leave in 1975 from musculo-skeletal sick leaves starting in 1974.
  The percentage shown for number of m-s diagnoses indicates number of m-s diagnoses as a fraction of man-labour years
  at 8B and cable making, respectively

man-labour years was reduced by a third (16.5% vs 24.5%, p<0.05) signifying that such complaints have become less frequent, but of longer duration. This is mainly due to a single sick leave with a duration of more than a year, accounting for 1.2% of total sick leave after 1975 at the 8B system. Excluding this chance occurrence of a very long sick leave, musculo-skeletal sick leave at the 8B system in the years 1975 to 1981 was 3.3%, and clearly lower than average musculo-skeletal sick leave before the ergonomics adaptations.

Interviews and questionnaires

Workers employed before 1974 were interviewed in the autumn of 1978 regarding symptoms of musculo-skeletal illness 'before' and 'now' for various parts of the body (Westgaard and Aarås, 1984). Fig. 5 shows the highest indication of discomfort, regardless of body location, 'before' and 'now' for workers employed at the 8B system (A) and cable making (B). The workers at the 8B system were in part employed at 10C, 11B and Minimat when interviewed, but they had all had some experience with the 8B system after the ergonomics adaptations. There is a clear reduction of about 1 unit in level of discomfort from the past to the present situation for workers at the 8B system, but most workers had experienced some discomfort in their work situations last year (1979). There was also a reduction in discomfort among workers at cable making, and no one had experienced discomfort/pain of the upper two intensities.

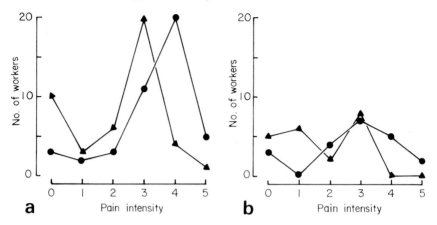

Figure 5   Highest indication of discomfort, regardless of body location, 'before' (●) and 'now' (▲) by workers employed before 1974 on the 8B system (A) and cable making (B).

Seventy five percent (41 of 55 persons) of those indicating reduced pain, when asked whether they associated (changes in) pain intensity with any external occurrences, were of the opinion that the ergonomics adaptations of their workplace had a significant effect on their wellbeing. Of the others (45 persons), 50% were of the opinion that the new workplaces were better, but felt little improvement with regard to the occurrence of pain. All workers had a positive attitude towards the new workplaces.

The workers were also asked to give their opinion of the reason for the reduction in musculo-skeletal illness in a questionnaire. They had to indicate whether they thought various factors were of very little, little, some or considerable significance. The answers are shown in Table 4. The factor considered to be most important by the workers was the possibility of altering the height and slope of the work table (93%). Almost as many thought that "easier to change work posture" and the introduction of a fixed pay structure were important (83 and 73%, respectively). It is of course difficult to separate the groups 'possible to alter height and slope of work table' and 'easier to change work posture'. The main conclusion from the interviews was that the workers had a very positive attitude towards the ergonomics adaptations. The introduction of fixed pay was also considered to be of major significance for the reduction in musculo-skeletal sick leave, presumably because the workers were more able to relax in their work situation.

The workers were also asked to indicate what they thought could be the reason for the reduction in labour turn-over, and 50 workers (57%) thought that an improved work environment was the most important reason (Table 5). Thus, there was a strong feeling among the workers that the work environment at the factory had improved. This is probably due to both the ergonomics adaptations and to improved co-operation between workers and the management which in turn arose from the intensive environmental work programme at STK (Aarås and Westgaard, 1980).

Productivity

The development of productivity at STK Kongsvinger is shown for cable making (Fig. 6, open circles) and all other work systems combined (Fig. 6, filled circles). The values are shown in relative units, using an estimate of standard time for a well

Table 4   The workers' views on the reasons for the reduction in musculo-skeletal sick leave. The evaluation is based on a questionnaire to 87 workers

	No significance		Little significance		Some significance		Considerable significance		Total	
	No	%	No	%	No	%	No	%	No	%
Introduction of flexible working hours	27	32	13	15	16	19	28	33	84	99
Introduction of a fixed pay structure	3	4	6	7	13	15	61	73	83	99
Easier to alter the height and slope of the work table	1	1	1	1	4	5	77	93	83	100
Easier to change work posture	1	1	2	3	11	14	66	83	80	101
Easier to have short pauses	4	5	14	17	30	36	35	42	83	100
New sick leave benefit system	34	42	20	25	17	21	10	12	81	100
Other	—	—	—	—	2	—	2	—	4	—

Table 5   The workers' views on the reasons for the reduction in turn-over. The significance of different factors is indicated as 1 — important, 2 — less important, 3 — may be significant

	Significance (number of indications)		
Reason	1	2	3
Difficult to obtain alternative employment	11	11	1
The pay rate is good	25	12	1
Improved work environment	50	8	2
Other	1	2	1
Total	87	33	5

defined unit of work as a basis. The values for 8B, Minimat, 10C and 11B are not strictly comparable from year to year, since most of the work was carried out on the 8B system before 1975, while 10C, 11B and Minimat production dominated the last few years. However, the development of productivity at the four systems combined has been very similar to that of cable making, where the work tasks have remained unchanged from 1967 to 1983. In addition to the ergonomics adaptations, the introduction of a fixed pay system appears to have had a major influence on productivity. Fig. 6 shows that productivity initially was fairly low, then increasing rapidly from 1973 onwards. The ergonomics adaptations were implemented towards the end of this incline, but productivity remained high for at least one year afterwards. This was the first year with a marked drop in long-term sick leave, and it is important to note that the reduced sick leave was not due to less effort at work. It is also interesting (although not unexpected) to note that the highest level of productivity happened in the quarter which determined the level of wages in the fixed pay system, followed by a marked drop for a period after the introduction of

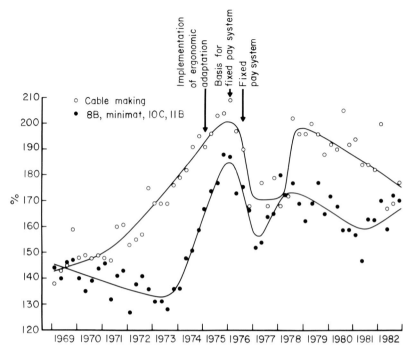

Figure 6   Productivity at cable making (○) and the rest of the production systems (●). Productivity is shown relative to a nominal production norm.

fixed pay. This was followed by a sharp incline in productivity in 1978 and a slow reduction in the years 1979 to 1981 which continued in 1982 for cable making, but increasing again in 1982 for the other systems. However, the main point of interest for the purpose of this paper is that productivity has on average been higher during the years following the ergonomics adaptations than the years preceding these.

Discussion

Following the implementation of ergonomics adaptations to the workplaces at STK Kongsvinger in the beginning of 1975, a period of several years with increasing long-term sick leave was ended. A reduction in long-term sick leave of a third followed, from 16.9% of possible working time in 1974 to 10.0% in 1975. This reduction was mainly due to a reduction in musculo-skeletal sick leave. There was also a reduction in labour turn-over. Workers with experience of both the old and the new work situations reported less severe symptoms of musculo-skeletal complaints (in 1978), and they were of the opinion that this was mainly due to the introduction of new workplaces. It has been demonstrated that mean muscle loads of the affected muscles in some cases were reduced by about 50% when comparing the new work situations with the old ones. Finally, the workers have on average been more productive (i.e., they have been working faster) after the introduction of new workplaces.

This evidence strongly suggests that the intensive work environmental effort at STK (Aarås and Westgaard, 1980), with a bias towards ergonomics adaptations of the workplace, has had a clear, positive effect. However, at this time it is of interest to consider the effect of ergonomics adaptations as such, rather than the effect of more general changes in working conditions. The analysis was therefore further extended by attempting to eliminate the effects of a product development, which resulted in new work situations for many workers independently of the ergonomics efforts. At two work systems, the 8B system and cable making, a sufficient number of workers was employed before and after the ergonomics adaptations to allow a direct comparison of sick leave. Workers at cable making recorded a clear reduction in total long-term sick leave and musculo-skeletal sick leave in the years 1975 to 1982, relative to the years 1967 to 1974. Thus, the conclusions based on evidence from the factory as a whole are also valid for workers at cable making in particular, and it appears reasonable to attribute the cause of this development to the ergonomics adaptations. A possible complication is the introduction of fixed pay in May 1976, but the reduction in sick leave was established much before then. This, together with the workers' opinions on probable causes for the improvement in their health situation, makes the change in pay structure a less important explanation, although it almost certainly has made a positive contribution towards the improved health of the workers.

The situation at the 8B system is less clear. Sick leave due to musculo-skeletal complaints was not much reduced in the years 1975 to 1980 (4.6%), relative to the years 1967 to 1974 (5.1%), but was significantly reduced relative to musculo-skeletal sick leave in 1973 and 1974 (6.9% and 9.1%, Table 2 of Westgaard and Aarås, 1984), and this may be a better basis for comparison. Furthermore, musculo-skeletal sick leave in 1975 to 1980 was reduced to 3.3% of possible working time if a single sick leave is excluded, and this represents a significant reduction compared with previous years. The number of sick leaves with musculo-skeletal diagnoses, in percent of man-labour years, is also down (16.5 vs 24.5%, Table 3). Many of the workers ill with musculo-skeletal complaints at the 8B system from 1975 onwards had suffered a similar complaint while working at the old workplace. This would normally reduce the tolerance to further muscle strain, and may contribute to increased sick leave. Thus the impression is that even for workers at the 8B system there has been a reduction in sick leave from musculo-skeletal complaints, presumably signifying improved health of this group of workers. The reported reduction in relevant symptoms and the workers' opinions of the effect of the ergonomics adaptations lent further support to this notion.

However, the effect of the ergonomics adaptations at the 8B system was less obvious than at cable making. This could be due to the fact that cable making is a dynamic work situation, while the new 8B work situation still demanded a fairly high static muscle load, although substantially reduced relative to the old one. The EMG recordings suggested a reduction in static muscle load from about 20% to 10% of maximal voluntary contraction. These values are very uncertain due to the lack of correlation with force, but there is every reason to suspect that the level of static muscle load is much higher than a recommended upper limit of 3–5% MVC, suggested by others (Bjørksten and Jonsson, 1977). We therefore conclude that the ergonomics adaptations have had a clear positive effect even for the 8B system, but without further reducing the level of static muscle load, musculo-skeletal complaints are likely to continue albeit at a lower rate.

A final comment regarding the continuing, quite high level of long-term sick leave in the latter years despite the substantial reduction in sick leave due to musculo-skeletal complaints. This is mainly due to the chance occurrence of a few sick leaves of about one year duration (neurological and other illnesses), which each account for nearly 1% of possible working days lost through sick leave.

References

AARÅS, A, and WESTGAARD, R.H. (1980). *Ergonomics*, **23**, 707–726. The organisation and execution of work environmental projects in a Norwegian industrial company.

BIGLAND, B., and LIPPOLD, O.C.J. (1954). *J Physiol*, **123**, 214–224. The relation between force, velocity and integrated electrical activity in human muscles.

BJØRKSTEN, M., and JONSSON, B. (1977). *Scand J Work Environ & Health*, **3**, 23–27. Endurance limit of force in long-term intermittent static contractions.

CHAFFIN, D.B., LEE, M., and FREIVALDS, A. (1980). *Med Sci Sports Exercise*, **12**, 205–211. Muscle strength assessment from EMG analysis.

KOMI, P.V., and VIITASALO, J.H.T. (1976). *Acta Physiol Scand*, **96**, 267–276. Signal characteristics of EMG at different levels of muscle tension.

LINDSTRÖM, L., MAGNUSSON, R., and PETERSEN, I. (1974). *Scand J Rehab Med*, **3**, 127–148. Muscle load influence on myoelectric signal characteristics.

WESTGAARD, R.H., and AARÅS, A. (1984). *Applied Ergonomics*, **15.3**, 162–174. Postural muscle strain as a causal factor in the development of musculo-skeletal illness.

The theory and practice of safe handling temperatures

R. D. Ray

Robert Gordon's Institute of Technology, Aberdeen

Many hot objects which may be touched or handled every day can cause either discomfort, pain or burning of the skin. The precise effect will depend on the Contact Temperature t_c, an intermediate value between the hot object and the skin temperature. The value of t_c varies with the material, and is governed by the Contact Coefficient b, a property of the material which has a wide range of values from metals to plastics. In the experiments with 48 female subjects, surface and contact temperatures for three materials were measured over a wide range, and subject reactions recorded on a five-point comfort scale. From the heat conduction theory outlined, and using the calculated values of b for the three materials, the predicted safe surface temperatures were determined. These predicted values were then compared with the observed temperatures and with those recommended in British Standards.

Introduction

It is well known that many items of domestic equipment in everyday use require that some parts at least be maintained at a higher than ambient temperature in order to perform their function properly. Obvious examples are the cooker and hob, a clothes iron, kettles, heating radiators and fires, in the sphere of appliances using some form of fuel. Smaller items such as saucepans, coffee and tea pots, dishes and casseroles used in the oven also reach high temperatures due to external heating. All of these appliances can present a heat hazard, and have given rise to a large number of burning injuries in the home. It is estimated that hospitals in the United Kingdom annually treat more than 100 000 burns from these sources. In addition, there is a larger number of burns in the home of a less serious nature, 'nuisance burns', which can be treated locally by the householder. Other surfaces on appliances which may cause burns are those which people do not expect to get hot, but may in fact do so due to their proximity to high temperature sources or poor insulation, e.g., pan handles, oven doors, control knobs, etc. Whilst their temperatures may not rise to the same level as those in the previous category, the effect may for all that be regarded as objectionable.

The effect on the human body when it comes into contact with high temperature surfaces is clearly variable, but has been classified according to degree as follows:

(a) Injury by burning of the skin and underlying tissue.
(b) Pain to an extent that a person quickly releases contact.
(c) Discomfort such that a person can maintain contact for only a short time.

It was only in 1966, however, that a British Standard was written to try to limit these unpleasantly high temperatures in domestic appliances. In this standard, an attempt was made to classify hot surfaces according to their function; thus we have:

(a) Surfaces designed to be held in the hand.
(b) Surfaces which are only briefly handled.
(c) Surfaces which may be touched accidentally.
(d) Other heated surfaces.

197

Recommendations for limiting the temperatures of various surfaces are given in the standard for these categories. They do, however, depend on the material used, and reference is made to this later. Some typical temperatures frequently encountered in the home and which are likely to come into contact with the body are shown below:

Hot tap water .... 60°C
Shower water .... 44°C
Metal pan handle .... up to   80°C
Plastic pan handle .... up to   60°C
Oven door .... 60 to   90°C
Heating radiator ....70 to   80°C
Dish in oven .... 120 to 150°C
Electric lamp 150 W ....170°C

While injury or pain are important issues, avoiding discomfort is perhaps the more appropriate factor to be considered in the design of parts of the appliance or equipment which has to be handled. It would therefore be an advantage to be able to predict a safe or comfortable temperature for various surfaces under different conditions.

Heat transfer to the skin

When a part of the body comes into contact with a hot object which is at a temperature above the skin temperature, heat will flow by conduction from the object into the skin and tissues causing the temperature to rise. The extent of this rise will depend on the nature and temperature of the object, the duration of contact, and the area of contact. The effect depending on these factors will be a sensation of warmth, discomfort, pain or burning of the skin.

The thermal process involved in this case is one of unsteady or transient heat conduction, such that with the passage of time, the interface temperature between the hot object and the skin attempts to reach a stable value. This value which lies between the object temperature t_h and the initial skin temperature t_s is known as the contact temperature t_c. It is this temperature which stimulates the heat sensors under the skin and causes a human reaction.

If the contact temperature t_c in a particular case is less or equal to some experimentally determined comfortable value, then the person will be able to maintain the contact or hold indefinitely, i.e., a comfortable handling condition exists. If the contact temperature rises just above this value, then contact can only be maintained for a very short time before the hold will have to be released. Still higher contact temperatures are likely to cause pain or even burning of the skin. The contact temperature, however, may not be the same for all materials, so that two materials may be at the same temperature, but depending on their thermal properties could give different contact temperatures when touched; an explanation of this is given later.

As stated earlier, the thermal conduction involved in this case is transient or unsteady, i.e., the temperature will change with respect to time. In the simpler steady state case, the rate of heat conduction per unit area q is governed by the temperature gradient with respect to thickness x, dt/dx, and the thermal conductivity λ of the material, thus $q = \lambda(dt/dx)$.

Transient conduction is more complex, and depends on three properties of the material, namely the density ϱ, the specific heat capacity c, as well as the thermal conductivity. This is expressed symbolically by the general form of Fourier's law thus,

$$\frac{\delta t}{\delta r} = \frac{\lambda}{\varrho.c} \cdot \frac{\delta^2 t}{\delta x^2}$$

where $\dfrac{\delta t}{\delta r}$ = rate of change of temperature with time

$\dfrac{\delta^2 t}{\delta x^2}$ = first derivative of the temperature gradient.

While this equation can be solved mathematically in some cases, it is more common to use graphical methods. For the practical purposes of this work, it is possible to arrive at an approximate solution following van der Held (1939), leading to an expression for a predicted safe surface temperature. The approach is to consider the heat transfers between an outer layer of the hot object, thickness x, and of a layer of skin, thickness y. The mass per unit area will be $x.\varrho_h$ for the material, and $y.\varrho_s$ for the skin, since the heat loss by the material = the heat gained by the skin.

	Hot object	Skin	
Rate of heat conduction	$q = \dfrac{\lambda h}{x} [t_h - t_c]$	$= \dfrac{\lambda s}{y} [t_c - t_s]$	... (1)
Net heat lost or gained in unit time	$q = x\varrho_h \cdot c_h [t_h - t_c]$	$= y\varrho_s c_s \cdot [t_c - t_s]$	... (2)

Combining these equations to eliminate x and y, then

$$[\lambda_h\varrho_h c_h]^{\frac{1}{2}} [t_h - t_c] = [\lambda_s\varrho_s c_s]^{\frac{1}{2}} [t_c - t_s] \qquad \text{... (3)}$$

The square root term in each case is a property of the material known as the contact coefficient $b = [\lambda.\varrho.c]^{\frac{1}{2}}$, thus,

$$b_h [t_h - t_c] = b_s [t_c - t_s] \qquad \text{... (4)}$$

where b_h = contact coefficient of the material
$\quad b_s$ = contact coefficient of the skin

Transposing equation (4) gives an expression for the safe surface temperature of a hot object in terms of the other variables

$$t_h = t_c + \frac{b_s}{b_h} [t_c - t_s] \qquad \text{... (5)}$$

Stoll, Chianta and Piergallini (1982) have used a transposed form of equation (5) to determine estimated values of contact temperatures at the skin pain threshold (i.e., 3 s contact), for several materials.

The contact coefficient as defined above is shown in many British Standards, though only in symbolic form and not explained or used. Typical values of contact coefficient b_h for some common materials are:

Aluminium	=	23 000 J/m² s$^{\frac{1}{2}}$°C
Steel	=	13 000 J/m² s$^{\frac{1}{2}}$°C
Glass	=	1 460 J/m² s$^{\frac{1}{2}}$°C
Plastics	=	500–800 J/m² s$^{\frac{1}{2}}$°C
Wood	=	510 J/m² s$^{\frac{1}{2}}$°C
Cork	=	480 J/m² s$^{\frac{1}{2}}$°C

In BS 3456 part 101:1978, materials are arranged into three classes according to the values of b, the units being J/m² $s^{\frac{1}{2}}$°C.

values of b greater than 3500 .... metals
values of b between 1000 and 3500 .... porcelain and vitreous material
values of b less than 1000 .... moulded materials, rubber and wood.

An indication of how the properties of the material in the form of the contact coefficient affect the contact temperature t_c, and hence the likely human reaction, is shown in Fig. 1. It is also necessary to establish a value b_s for the skin and tissues. The values of λ_s, ϱ_s and c_s for human skin vary in different parts of the body, so that van der Held (1939) and Buettner (1951) have tended to quote values of b_s directly between 1100 and 1300 J/m² $s^{\frac{1}{2}}$°C for the hand. Stolwijk and Hardy (1965) give the following values for the hand, $\varrho_s = 0.86$ g/cm³, $c_s = 1.2$ cal/g °C, with $\lambda_s = 0.001$ cal/cm s °C for the inner layers of the skin to $\lambda_s = 0.005$ cal/cm s °C for the outer layers. This gives a range of values of b_s of 3.6 × 10⁻² $s^{\frac{1}{2}}$°C (1400 J/m² $s^{\frac{1}{2}}$°C) to 1.8 × 10⁻² cal/cm² $s^{\frac{1}{2}}$°C [700 J/m² $s^{\frac{1}{2}}$°C]. For the purposes of this work, a value of 1100 J/m² $s^{\frac{1}{2}}$°C will be used for b_s.

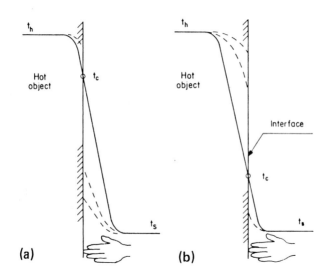

Figure 1   Effect of b value on contact temperature
t_c $(b - [\lambda \varrho c]^{\frac{1}{2}})$
(a) Material A — high b value
(b) Material B — low b value.

Experimental method

For the practical purposes of product design, it is required to estimate the maximum temperature of an object to be handled or a surface that may be touched which the human hand could reasonably tolerate. In accordance with the categories of contact already mentioned, the main object of the work was to determine a comfortable surface temperature for different materials, for brief and prolonged contact. Thus a range of material temperatures had to be measured so that they could be related to the comfort reactions of people when contact was made. Also, in order to predict comfortable surface temperatures from the theory, simultaneous measurements of skin and contact temperature were required.

Hand skin temperatures were measured with both a skin thermistor bead, recording through a Minilab electronic thermometer and a light spring-loaded probe of a chromel–alumel thermocouple connected to an analogue temperature indicator. For contact temperatures bare fine wire chromel–alumel thermocouples were used, and another spring probe for the material temperature, each being connected to an analogue indicator. All of these instruments had a resolution of 1 degree C, and had mean responses of about 5 degrees per second. This response was really important only when contact temperatures were measured for the brief contact condition.

To record human reactions to thermal contact, it was decided to construct a verbal comfort scale. Lele, Weddell and Williams (1954) in their work on thermal irradiation of the hand used an 8-point scale from Nothing (1) to Intolerable Pain (8), but for the practical purposes of this work a shorter 5-point scale was devised as follows:

Thermal comfort scale

Vote	Description	Effect
1	No noticeable thermal sensation	None
2	Comfortably warm	Thermal sensation but no discomfort
3	Comfortably hot	Contact maintained for at least 30 s, i.e. prolonged contact
4	Very hot	Contact possible for short time only (approx 3 s) i.e. brief contact
5	Unbearably hot	Thermal discomfort or pain, (immediate release of contact).

The experiments were carried out with 48 young female subjects, having an age range of 18 to 22 years. At this age, their hands were not noticeably calloused, though they had worked regularly in domestic kitchens, and thus were accustomed to handling hot materials. Three discs 15 cm in diameter were made of the materials aluminium, wood, and a thermosetting plastic (phenol formaldehyde), typically used in many domestic products; each disc had a smooth surface. The discs were heated in turn on an electrically heated hot plate over an appropriate range of temperatures for a given material.

The subjects were instructed to make contact with the hot disc with the lateral surface of the index finger at each temperature level. This area was regarded as the most vulnerable part of the hand in most types of handle grip. Starting at 30°C, between 10 and 12 levels of surface temperature were considered depending on the material. The surface temperature of the material and the skin temperature midway between the interphalangeal joints of the lateral side of the index finger were measured simultaneously using the probes. The subject then immediately made contact with the material using a light pressure, the fine wire thermocouple being inserted between the skin and material and held there by pressure. An early attempt to insert the thermocouple in the outer layer of the skin was abandoned as it seemed to make little difference to the measurements and probably would not have been acceptable to the subjects.

After an appropriate contact time, the subject was asked to give a comfort vote corresponding to the descriptions given in the comfort scale. When a brief contact was expected, the thermocouple was held at skin temperature prior to the measurement in order to improve the response time. Between each measurement, time was allowed for the soft tissue of the finger to resume its normal shape and the skin temperature to return to normal. Only at comfort vote 5 was it obviously not possible to measure contact temperature.

A similar set of measurements was made on saucepan handles, one being of aluminium and another with a plastic insulated handle. The pans containing water were allowed to simmer until there was a range of temperatures along the handles. The subjects then made the same contacts as before, starting at the cooler end of the handle and progressing towards the pan end. The surfaces of both handles were again smooth. No attempt was made in either of these trials to increase the pressure of contact, i.e. only the pressure of a light grip was used.

The ambient temperature of the room during the experiments ranged from 20°C to 22°C.

Experimental results

Although a full set of measurements was made, only those corresponding to prolonged and brief contact were the main concern of this work and are reported here. For both the aluminium and the plastic material, the measurements for the discs and the pan handles were combined to give overall mean values and the variation. The means and standard deviations for the contact temperature and the material temperature for each material at brief and prolonged contact are given in Table 1.

For the brief contact condition, the means of the contact temperature for the aluminium, phenol formaldehyde and wood were 50, 46 and 47°C respectively with standard deviations of ± 6% whereas Stoll, Chianta and Piergallini (1979, 1982)

Table 1   **Comparison of safe handling temperatures with various materials and two contact conditions**

| | Material | | | | | | | |
| | Aluminium | | Glass | | Phenol formaldehyde | | Wood | |
Comfort condition	Mean °C	SD °C	Mean °C	SD °C	Mean °C	SD °C	Mean °C	SD °C
Prolonged contact (at least 30 s duration)								
Contact temperature t_c	43	3	—	—	42	2	43	2
Material temperature	48	2.5	—	—	59	4	56	3
Predicted tolerable material temperature t_h	44	—	52	—	64	—	68	—
Recommended maximum surface temperature BS 4086: 1966	55	—	65	—	75	—	75	—
Brief contact (3 s duration)								
Contact temperature t_c	50	3	—	—	46	3	47	3
Material temperature	55	3	—	—	66	3	63	3
Predicted tolerable material temperature t_h	51	—	59	—	71	—	76	—
Recommended maximum surface temperature BS 4086: 1966	60	—	68	—	85	—	85	—

Skin temperature on lateral side of index finger midway between interphalangeal joints
For 48 subjects: Mean value = 31°C: SD = 1.3°C

give 50°C for aluminium, and 48°C for the plastics material teflon, with about the same variation. Considering that the subjects in the latter case were two men and two women of no stated age, compared with the young female subjects used here, the similarity in the findings was quite marked. Thus it seems that the contact temperatures for a given contact condition are almost the same regardless of the material used.

For the prolonged contact case, the contact temperatures as expected were a few degrees less than the previous case, the mean values for the three materials being 43, 42 and 43°C respectively, with standard deviations again about ± 6%. These are slightly lower than the 45°C suggested by van der Held (1942), though in this case, the nature of the contact was not specified and experimental results not given.

Using the mean values of skin and contact temperatures, for each material and for both contact conditions, predicted values of tolerable material surface temperatures were calculated from equation (5). Thus, for example, for the phenol formaldehyde plastic with properties taken from Chong (1977) as follows $\lambda = 0.17$ W/m °C, $\varrho = 1320$ kg/m^3, $c = 1460$ J/kg °C, the contact coefficient b_h is given by $b_h = [0.17 \times 1320 \times 1460]^{\frac{1}{2}} = 572$ J/m^2 s$^{\frac{1}{2}}$°C. If b_s is assumed to be 1100 J/m^2 s$^{\frac{1}{2}}$°C, then the ratio

$b_s/b_h = \dfrac{1100}{572} = 1.92$, which is of the same order as the value used for teflon

(i.e., 1.82) by Stoll, Chianta and Piergallini (1982) to determine predicted contact temperatures for brief contacts. Thus taking $t_s = 31$°C, with $t_c = 42$°C for prolonged contact, and $t_c = 46$°C for brief contact, then the predicted tolerable material temperatures are as follows.

Prolonged contact   Brief contact

$t_h = t_c + \dfrac{b_s}{b_h} [t_c - t_s]$ $t_h = t_c + \dfrac{b_s}{b_h} [t_c - t_s]$

$t_h = 42 + \dfrac{1100}{572} [42 - 31]$ $t_h = 46 \dfrac{1100}{572} [46 - 31]$

$\quad = 63$°C $\quad = 73$°C

Similar values for other materials, together with the recommended maximum material surface temperatures from BS 4086: 1966, are given in Table 1 for comparison; see also Fig. 2. A column has been included for glass, an intermediate material, to compare the predicted surface temperature with those in BS 4086: 1966, even though no experimental values are available at this stage.

The predicted tolerable surface temperatures t_h found from theory showed a variation between materials, reflecting the different order of contact coefficients; thus the plastics material and the wood gave similar values. The observed surface temperatures were also of the same order though several degrees lower. For the aluminium, it was the reverse, the predicted value of t_h being slightly less than the observed values for both contact conditions. In all cases, the predicted and observed surface temperatures were lower than the current recommendations in BS 4086: 1966.

Conclusions

The results of this experimental work have given some indication of human responses to skin contact with hot materials under various times of contact. It was seen that materials of low contact coefficient could be tolerated at surface temperatures some 20 degrees C higher than metallic materials with high coefficients. Wood

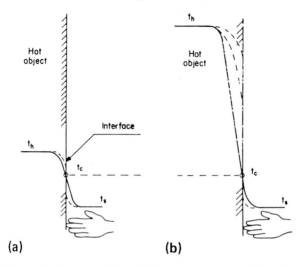

Figure 2 Two materials at different temperatures giving the same contact temperature t_c
(a) Material A — high b value
(b) Material B — low b value.

and the plastics material showed very similar effects in this respect. Also the various materials, though being at different temperatures, showed approximately the same contact temperature for a given contact time, implying the same thermal sensation, or in effect that they 'felt' at the same temperature. Although the predicted tolerable temperatures had values a few degrees different from the observed values, it should be possible for all practical purposes to make a reasonable estimation of tolerable surface temperature for any material if the properties are known, and the appropriate contact temperature is assumed.

Thus for applications where a prolonged hold is required such as all handles and grips on appliances, implements or tools, a lower contact temperature (i.e., 43°C) should be used. Where only brief contact is expected such as with switches, control knobs, pushbuttons, or other parts not normally touched in the task, a contact temperature of say 48–50°C could be used. If a designer cannot achieve a low enough material temperature, or is unable to use a suitable material to lower the contact temperature to a tolerable level, then protective wear must be provided for the hands. Finally, it will be noted that the British Standards recommendations are some 10–15 degrees C greater than either the observed or predicted values and possibly should be questioned.

References

BRITISH STANDARDS INSTITUTION (1966). BS 4086:1966, Recommendations for maximum surface temperatures of heated domestic equipment.

BRITISH STANDARDS INSTITUTION (1978). BS 3456: part 101: 1978, Safety of household and similar electrical appliances.

BUETTNER, K. (1951). *J Appl Physiol*, **3**, 703–713. Effects of extreme heat and cold on human skin, II. Surface temperatures, pain and heat conductivity in experiments with radiant heat.

CHONG, C.V.Y. (1977). *Properties of materials*. Macdonald and Evans, Plymouth.

VAN DER HELD, E.F.M. (1939). *Elektrowärme*, **9.2**, 31–34. Temperaturerhöhung von Handgriffen.

VAN DER HELD, E.F.M. (1942). *Schweiz. Blätter, f Heizung u Lüftung*, **9.1**, 18–19. Etwas über verbrannte Finger und kalte Füsse.

LELE, P.P., WEDDELL, G., and WILLIAMS, C.M. (1954). *J Physiol*, **126**, 206–234. The relationship between heat transfer, skin temperature and cutaneous sensibility.

STOLL, A.M, CHIANTA, M.A., and PERGALLINI, J.R. (1979). *Aviat Space Environ Med.* 50, 778–787. Thermal conduction effects in human skin.

STOLL, A.M., CHIANTA, M.A., and PIERGALLINI, J.R. (1982). *Aviat Space Environ Med.* **53**, 1220–1223. Prediction of threshold pain skin temperature from thermal properties of materials in contact.

STOLWIJK, J.A.J., and HARDY, J.D. (1965). *J Appl Physiol*, **20**, 1006–1013. Skin and subcutaneous temperature changes during exposure to intense thermal radiation.

Observations on in-house ergonomics training for first-line supervisors

L. A. Smith* and J. L. Smith†

* Associate Professor, Industrial Engineering Department, Auburn University, Alabama, USA
† Assistant Professor, Industrial Engineering Department, Texas Tech University, Lubbock, Texas, USA

Advantages of and approaches to in-house training of first-line supervisory personnel in the principles of ergonomics are discussed. Particular attention is given to the one- to three-day short course approach. The short course approach is illustrated by a case study summarising the authors' experiences in one multi-plant corporation over a period of five years. It is concluded that supervisory personnel typically respond positively to ergonomics instruction; that, to be successful, the course material must relate to situations in which the supervisor can exercise some control; and that the one- to three-day course format appears appropriate for such instruction.

Introduction

Various educational opportunities are available to persons wishing to obtain or improve their competencies in ergonomics. The largest portion of these is directed toward university students. The remaining educational opportunities are typically directed toward practising engineers, managers, industrial health personnel and military officers in the form of various short courses or extension activities offered by universities, professional societies, and government agencies. The content and conduct of these educational programmes have been described and discussed in the literature; example papers include: Halstead-Nussloch (1981), Pearson (1980), Bernotat and Hunt (1977), Corlett (1976), and Brown (1973). There appears to be no direct reference in the literature however to the topic of ergonomics education or training for first-line supervisors. In the opinion of the authors, these individuals could potentially contribute as much or more to the successful application of ergonomics principles as any other single group.

Several benefits would accrue to the production firm which trains supervisors in the basic principles and techniques of ergonomics. First, the training would give the supervisors a different perspective from which to view the tasks and workplaces under their control by making them aware of the types of occupational stress problems which may develop from inappropriate procedures, equipment, workplace designs, and work postures. Once aware, the supervisors should be able to prevent or correct many problems themselves; or at least, they would know when to call upon ergonomics, industrial hygiene, work study, or occupational safety personnel for help. Second, basic knowledge of ergonomics principles and techniques would assist supervisors in recognising and instituting improvements that could increase productivity directly or reduce the amount of time spent in non-productive activities. Third, basic knowledge of ergonomics should make supervisors more understanding and co-operative when task changes or new safety and health related work practices needed to be initiated since they would have a better appreciation of the reasons underlying the changes.

Four general approaches could be utilised for providing ergonomics training to supervisory personnel. First, the instruction could be presented through self-taught programmed instruction either in written or computerised format containing appropriate exercises. Second, the instruction could be provided as part of the content of regularly scheduled safety or production meetings attended by supervisors on a weekly or monthly basis. Third, the supervisors could be introduced to ergonomics through presentation of brief 'orientation' programmes of one-half to two hours' duration. Fourth, the material could be presented through supervisors attending special in-house 'short courses' of one or more days' length. This paper presents observations relative to the use of the last approach.

In-house ergonomics short courses

A paper by Rohmert and Laurig (1977) is the only entry in the literature to the authors' knowledge that discusses an in-house ergonomics short course whose attendees were at least partially composed of first-line supervisors. Rohmert and Laurig presented several offerings of a four-day course to individuals employed in seven plants of a German automobile manufacturing firm. Attendees included employees in charge, heads of sections, heads of departments, and division managers of upper level administrators. Among the topics in the course syllabus were work physiology, anthropometry/biomechanics, noise, lighting, environment in general, work place design, and system analysis and design. Various measures of the effectiveness of the course in producing both short term and long term benefits seemed to indicate that it was successful. Rohmert and Laurig concluded that the four-day short course format was a promising alternative between classical academic education and trial and error self-education for training in applied ergonomics. The reaction to the course of the 'employees in charge' is not specifically discussed.

An in-house short course case study

The authors performed a variety of ergonomics activities for a large textile manufacturing firm during the summer of 1977. It became apparent at an early stage of these activities that many small, fairly obvious (to the trained observer) man-machine incompatibilities existed that could have been corrected immediately by the concerned supervisory personnel if these individuals had possessed even a modest knowledge of ergonomics principles. Consequently, an ergonomics 'short course' for first-line supervisors was developed with the co-operation and administrative assistance of the corporate manpower development staff and the corporate industrial engineering group. The course has been taught annually since its development. Although developed and taught primarily for first-line supervisors, it has also been attended by industrial engineering, occupational medicine and training personnel.

Course development guidelines

The course was organised and the content selected under four general guidelines. These guidelines were based on the manpower development staff's experience in presenting training programmes on a variety of topics to supervisory personnel and on the authors' previous experience in ergonomics education. The guidelines are:

(1) The course subject matter and illustrative examples must be easily understood and must relate to practical situations in which the first-line supervisor could reasonably be expected to exercise some control.

(2) The course must be directed toward developing in supervisors the ability to recognise inconsistencies between task requirements and the performance capabilities of the individuals asked to perform those tasks.

(3) The course must encourage supervisors to attempt to reconcile ergonomics problems once they are recognised either by themselves or by seeking assistance from the corporation's professional industrial engineering, work study, industrial hygiene, or occupational safety staffs.

(4) The course must emphasise the potential benefits that would accrue to supervisors from the application of ergonomics in their work areas.

Course structure

The course contains approximately 14 h of instruction plus necessary breaks. The topics included and the coverage time for each topic are presented in Fig. 1. Both the topics and the coverage time for each have changed somewhat as experience has been gained with the course and it has been evaluated by the attendees. The topics and times illustrated by Fig. 1 represent the current course structure.

The course has been taught under two time schedules: (1) two consecutive full days and (2) four consecutive afternoons. A non-consecutive schedule has also been considered in which the course would be taught one day a week for two weeks or one afternoon a week for four weeks. Each of these schedules has advantages and disadvantages. The factors that must be considered when the schedule is selected include the ability of the supervisors (who typically are quite active at their work) to maintain their concentration in a rather passive classroom environment and the impact of the supervisor's absence from their jobs on the production process. An additional factor that must be considered when the course is spread over several days is the 'warm-up time' required each day to get the attendees back into a receptive frame of mind for instruction. Based on their experience to date, the authors prefer the two consecutive day format.

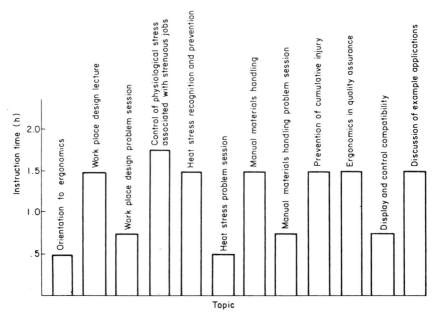

Figure 1 Topics covered in case-study ergonomics short course for supervisors.

Course presentation

The course presentation style is heavily influenced by the course development guidelines; that is, every effort is made to present the concepts in a manner that assists the supervisors in relating the course material to their work areas and responsibilities. Each topic presentation is illustrated with 35 mm slides or video-taped scenes of various work situations in the corporation's plants. Each illustrative problem and application pertains to a situation which could be resolved at the first-line supervisor's level of control. All discussions of the concepts presented are directed toward how supervisors can use ergonomics to enhance production and improve the quality of work life for the people under their charge. Each topic is also reinforced by providing the attendees with a neatly bound set of notes which they are expected to keep and use for later reference.

Course evaluation

Each time the course has been offered the attendees have been asked to complete course evaluation forms at the end of each day's session. The intent of the evaluations is to gauge the attendees' responses to the topics presented that day so as to determine which topics are most appropriate for supervisors and which need re-evaluation. As part of the evaluation process the attendees are asked to express agreement or disagreement with five statements concerning the applicability of ergonomics to the company's operations and ergonomics training within the company. The attendees are also encouraged to write any general comments about the course which they believe to be appropriate.

Analysis of the evaluations indicates that no one particular topic of those presented in Fig. 1 is considered inappropriate by the supervisors. On a relative basis the topics which have received the highest 'appropriateness' ratings are heat stress recognition and prevention, quality assurance, workplace design, and manual materials handling. Those that have been rated relatively lower are physiological stress, cumulative injury, and display and control compatibility. The essential element in the acceptability of the material to the supervisors is apparently the degree to which they believe they can use the information to enhance their jobs. The topics that are rated relatively higher are those that supervisors feel have the most direct impact upon themselves and are somewhat under their control. The course evaluations thus strongly reinforce the importance of course development guideline number 1.

A summary of the responses to the five agreement/disagreement statements is presented in Table 1. The responses to the statements indicate that all of the attendees believe ergonomics applications are needed within the company (statement 'a') and that roughly 94% believe they could be cost justified (statement 'c'). Approximately 90% of the attendees evaluate the course material as being useful to supervisors (statements 'b' and 'd'). The response to statement 'e' indicates that the supervisors feel very strongly that plant industrial engineering or work study personnel should become cognisant of ergonomics principles. The response to statement 'e' is most likely based on the supervisors' view that, whereas they can make significant contributions to job design, the plant industrial engineers or work study personnel are chiefly responsible for such activities.

The free response portion of the evaluations has resulted in numerous statements about the desirability of ergonomics instruction for supervisors. The statements contain suggestions as to the most effective group composition. The attendees seem unable to agree as to whether the course should be presented to groups composed

Table 1   Responses to 'Applicability' statements included in case-study course evaluation

INSTRUCTIONS: Please indicate whether you (1) strongly agree, (2) agree a little, (3) disagree a little, or (4) strongly disagree with each of the following statements:

Statement	*SA*	*A*	*DA*	*SDA*
(a) There is a need for ergonomics analysis of many (company name) work situations	53	47	0	0
(b) The supervisor is in a position to apply ergonomics information so as to improve work situations in his area	36	53	11	0
(c) Ergonomics activities could be cost justified in many (company name) work areas	37	57	6	0
(d) I recommend that other supervisors take an ergonomics course	40	50	10	0
(e) I recommend that plant IE's or work study personnel take an ergonomics course	82	18	0	0

of: (1) supervisors representing similar production activities in several different plants, (2) supervisors representing a mixture of production activities in several different plants, or (3) supervisors drawn from only a single production facility. The underlying concern seems to be which mixture would be most conducive to meaningful discussion of example applications. The free responses have also emphasised that the material presented in future courses must continue to relate to situations or aspects of the work environment under supervisory control.

A follow-up course evaluation has been conducted after two of the course offerings. Six months after the course was completed a questionnaire was mailed to each attendee by the corporation's manpower development office. Approximately 60% of the attendees of these courses completed and returned the forms. Since the forms were returned anonymously no effort could be made to track down the non-returned questionnaires. Likewise it was not possible to determine if the returned forms had been completed only by supervisors or if some of the non-supervisory personnel who have attended the courses responded.

Results of the follow-up questionnaires are presented in Fig. 2. The results and the additional comments appended to them indicated quite strongly that the attendees believed the courses to have been both beneficial to themselves and potentially beneficial to other supervisors. Six months after the course most of the respondents recommended that other supervisors take an ergonomics short course and all indicated that they had talked about the course and/or shared course information with others. Likewise, most of the respondents indicated that, during the six months that had elapsed since the course presentation, they had recognised problems that could be resolved by application of the ergonomics information presented and had taken action to resolve the recognised problems. Thus the course has had a positive impact at the job site.

The follow-up questionnaire also contained a multiple choice question in which the respondents were to indicate whether, assuming an ergonomics course continued to be offered by the corporation, it should be (1) a one to two hour orientation, (2) a course similar to the one they took lasting more than one day, or (3) a one-day course with content somewhere between choice (1) and (2). Fifty-seven per cent of the attendees who completed the follow-up questionnaires responded with choice (2); the remaining 43% of the responses were evenly divided between choices (1) and (3). Thus the majority of these course attendees believed

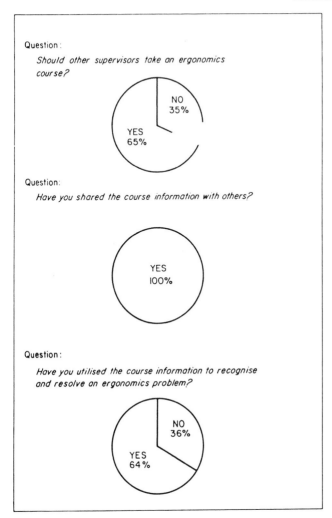

Figure 2   Results of case-study short course follow-up questionnaire.

that an ergonomics course for supervisors should be more than just an orientation to the topics and that a duration of at least one full day was appropriate.

Conclusions

Neither the literature nor the authors' limited experience in presenting ergonomics instruction to supervisors from several plants of one corporation provide an adequate basis on which to compare the instruction approaches identified. However, four general conclusions do seem appropriate in view of the authors' personal experience. First, supervisory personnel respond positively to ergonomics instruction. Apparently supervisors view ergonomics as something that can help them do their job more effectively and/or something that can assist them in resolving day to day problems. Second, a course format that provides more detailed instruction than that which could be accomplished in a short orientation programme is an appropriate approach and, indeed, may be preferred. Third, the course development guidelines followed in the authors' case study appear valid to the goal of structuring a meaningful course for supervisors. Further, it appears that the development guideline which states that the course lecture and problem sessions must relate to practical situations in which the supervisor could reasonably be expected to exercise some control is probably the most important. Fourth, training supervisors in ergonomics can show positive benefits to the firm. A majority of the attendees responding to a follow-up questionnaire reported applications of their ergonomics training in their own work areas either directly by themselves or by calling higher management's attention to the potential problems they were able to identify.

References

BERNOTAT, R., and HUNT, D.P. (1977). "University Curricula in Ergonomics". Forschungsinstitut fur Anthropotechnik, 5309 Meckenheim, Germany.

BROWN, E.S. (1973). Human factors concepts for management. Proceedings, 17th annual meeting of the Human Factors Society, Santa Monica, California, 327–375.

CORLETT, E.N. (1976). Ergonomics in industry, and the teaching relevant to the practice of industrial ergonomics. Proceedings, 6th congress of the International Ergonomics Association, Santa Monica, California, 33–36.

HALSTEAD-NUSSLOCH, R. (1981). A computer-based undergraduate course in human factors. Proceedings, 25th annual meeting of the Human Factors Society, Santa Monica, California, 243–244.

PEARSON, R.G. (1980). *Ergonomics*, **23.8**, 797–808. Educational programmes in ergonomics: A world-wide profile.

ROHMERT, W., AND LAURIG, W. (1977). *Applied Ergonomics*, **8.1**, 19–21. Increasing awareness of ergonomics by in-company courses — a case study.

Making human factors effective in industry: Examples from business telephone systems

E. T. Klemmer* and D. J. Dooling†

* Johns Hopkins University, Communications Research Laboratory, Baltimore, Maryland, USA
† A T & T Information Systems, Freehold, New Jersey, USA

Contributions by human factors to all phases of the product development cycle are illustrated by work done on business telephone systems. The work includes surveys of customer needs, laboratory tests of alternative physical designs and control procedures, development of efficient and effective instructional methods, field studies of delivery systems, and field evaluations of the final product. It is also demonstrated that data from applied studies can lead to general principles which are useful in other situations. Finally, suggestions are given about effective timing and organisational structure for human factors work.

Introduction

Human factors engineering is often thought of in terms of the physical design of equipment to make it easier for people to use. While such a definition is not wrong, it is much too limited with respect to what human factors specialists can do, and indeed have done at Bell Laboratories. This paper illustrates the variety of contributions that human factors people can make to engineering projects. We do this by using concrete illustrations from the development of new business telephone systems. In the process, we describe organisational and professional issues that facilitate or inhibit human factors effectiveness. The paper ends with some human factors principles that can be applied to work on future systems.

The central theme of this paper is that human factors specialists can add and should contribute to decisions at every stage of the system development cycle. We support this thesis with concrete examples of how human factors contributes to the following stages of development:

- Customer studies to define new services.
- Physical design of equipment.
- Design of operating procedures for users.
- Instructions and training.
- Delivery and operational support systems.
- System evaluation with customers in the field.

By describing specific 'success stories' at each of the above stages we hope to encourage a broader view of human factors. While all of our examples are taken from the area we know best, i.e., business telephone systems, we believe that the points made can be generalised to a wide range of engineering problem areas.

Customer studies to define new services

One activity that has been pursued by human factors psychologists at Bell Laboratories is the study of customer needs. The purpose of such studies is to ensure that the customer's perspective is represented in the design of products and services. Human factors work on customer studies takes us close to the domain of market research. There are, however, some specific differences between human factors studies of customer needs and market research. Marketing studies for business telephone systems tend to focus on the person who makes purchasing decisions on communications equipment. The emphasis is on finding out what that person wants to buy and on defining the 'willingness to pay'. Often, such studies focus on feature capabilities (e.g. '3-way conference calling') and not the detailed needs of specific users (e.g. secretaries need to know whether to pass a call to a busy principal). Human factors studies focus on the end user and attempt to uncover customer needs that can be met by the design of new features.

The typical methodology of a customer study consists of desk-to-desk interviews with users about their communications needs. Questions focus on problems that arise from present features on existing systems and solicit enough information about user communication in general that a picture of the company's problem areas can be constructed. It is generally not beneficial to ask people what new features or services they want. Users are uncreative at inventing new features. By mapping out communications patterns in a business and by identifying existing problem areas, customer studies can provide a data base for testing the applicability of new services.

An example of a successful customer study is one conducted in 1974 by Stephen Chechosky, Heidi Muench and Nick Valcoff. (When a study is cited, as here, without a specific reference, we are reporting conclusions from Bell Laboratories memoranda that are not available for public distribution.) They studied the needs of small business customers, businesses with 20 to 100 telephones. One hundred and thirty businesses in Delaware and Pennsylvania were visited and interviews were conducted with hundreds of end users. One of their key findings identified the need for quick call passing. Small companies often passed calls from a central answering attendant by holding the call and placing an intercom call to the destination party, a slow, cumbersome procedure. Customers who had the (then) new COM KEY key telephone system found the Voice Signalling feature very effective for fast call passing. Voice Signalling permits the attendant to announce the call over a loud-speaker in the recipient's telephone. Small businesses tend to have everyone share lines and the Voice Signalling feature is useful for announcing which line to pick up. There were some users who also had a need to talk back to the attendant without a major interruption of their ongoing activity (which could be talking on the telephone). This need was met by adding a 'Hands-Free Answer' feature which activates a microphone in the recipient's telephone. This is just one example of the contribution that customer studies can make to the choice of products, features and services. Any one study will contribute to a number of such decisions.

Customer studies are an example of human factors specialists making a contribution 'up front' in the design process. Handling one problem upstream avoids many later.

Physical design

There are many examples of contributions of human factors to the physical design of the user interface. Indeed, human factors at Bell Laboratories had its earliest impact on physical design questions such as the dots on the rotary dial, the weight of the handset, and the layout of the Touch-tone® pad as described in Hanson (1983, in press). A more recent contribution was an experiment by Spencer and King in 1981 on alternative button technologies for the push-button telephone. Data from this experiment demonstrated that low-force, moderate-travel buttons of one technology were superior to six other technologies in speed, accuracy and user preference. This study directly affected decisions on dialpads for the next generation of business telephone systems.

In addition to specific designs, some general principles came out of the work on physical design. For example, it is usually good to reduce the physical work required of the user (lighter handsets, low-force buttons). Feedback from the system should be given for each operation. Other findings relate to the slope of the faceplate, geometry of the handset, brightness of visual indicators, the coding of auditory signals, etc. These principles provide some guidance for new designs, but it is generally necessary to evaluate each specific new design by conducting tests with role-playing subjects.

Operating procedures

It has been our experience that operating procedures are even more important than physical design. They are also more important than user instructions, a topic we will address below. Historically, there has been little freedom to change control procedures for electro-mechanical systems and the procedures were fairly simple. That does not mean that there were no problems. The requirement to 'flash the switchhook' (press the hang-up button for one second) has been a continuing problem for users who are trying to signal the operator or transfer calls. The problem occurs because too short a 'flash' has no effect and too long a 'flash' leads to a disconnect. This problem is now solved by electronic key telephone systems that provide a button ('Recall') that works properly with presses of any duration.

Software controlled systems (where the telephone switching system is effectively a computer) provide a great deal of freedom in designing control procedures for feature operation. These systems also offer a wealth of new possible features. This represents a great challenge to the human factors specialist. It is not possible to optimise the procedures for each feature separately and still have logical consistency among all features, particularly when features can be used together in combination. Moreover, the flexibility in both number of features and control procedures means that there are a limitless number of alternative procedures which might be tested.

One example of human factors work on control procedures was a study on conferencing procedures done by Terry Spencer in 1979. Spencer conducted a series of tests with simulated systems and role-playing subjects in order to pick the best user procedures for the next generation of business telephones. The question, "What is the best method for setting up a three-way conference call?", may seem to be straightforward, but an analysis of the problem indicates a great deal of complexity and a significant number of decisions to be made. For example, should the first party to a conference be held while the second party is called, or should the first party be bridged on the call? If a hold feature is implemented as part of a conference feature, should the selection of the line for the next call be automatic, or should the user manually select the appropriate facility? How should a conference call be represented on a multi-button key telephone: one person per button or all conferees on one line button? How should a drop-from-conference feature work: can you select which of the parties to drop, or should a single button press automatically drop the most recent added party? In present products, both sides of each of the above issues are represented.

Spencer considered these questions (and many others) and chose 16 conference methods for human factors testing. Each tested procedure was one that appeared to be a good procedure to someone. There were no 'straw man' control procedures. The data for 'fatal' errors, i.e., dropping a call, failure to complete a problem, etc., showed striking differences among the procedures. Fatal errors varied from 4% to 24%. This proves the importance of control procedures in user performance. It should also be pointed out that fatal errors alone are not a sufficient basis for a decision. Some of the low-error procedures, while preventing serious errors, led to a high number of non-fatal errors and were not particularly convenient to use. The final decision on the best control procedures for conferencing was based on the results from several dependent variables. For another example of human factors work on control procedures, see Dooling (1980).

Instructions and training

Good instructions can never completely overcome difficulties due to design deficiencies but instructions are an increasingly important aspect of human factors work. As systems have more capabilities, there are more features to learn. Also, the cost of instructing users by conventional methods (live trainers, small classes, and hands-on practice) becomes prohibitively expensive. The introduction of communications systems which the customers themselves can program makes training considerations even more critical.

A striking example of the contribution that human factors work can make to instructional methods is the study done by Ellis (1977) on the training of users of the 'Dimension'® PBX telephone system. (See also Ellis and Coskren, 1979.) Laboratory tests with experimental subjects and first field installations showed that it required between one and two hours of time in conventional classes to introduce the system to individual users. This was judged too expensive both by the telephone companies and by the businesses being trained in terms of scheduling difficulties and lost time. A series of laboratory studies was conducted searching for ways to improve the training procedures. The most promising approaches from these studies were evaluated in field experiments involving actual users of the new system. These experiments showed that training time could be cut in half without reducing the level of customer feature use and feature knowledge.

We believe that the principles coming out of these studies can be applied to many situations involving procedural instructions. The principles are:

1. Hands-on training is not required for cognitive skills such as operating a feature-rich telephone system. Laboratory studies with subjects and field experiments with actual customers have failed to show an advantage for the hands-on approach. This finding allows for both larger class sizes and a reduction in time per class.
2. Initial training should introduce system capability and teach the use of performance aids (e.g. instruction card). It should not attempt to teach all operating procedures for all features. This finding allows for significant reduction in class time. It also reduces user frustration and confusion. The validity of the principle is demonstrated by the fact that even after two hours of conventional training, users typically did not understand all the specific feature procedures.
3. A third principle demonstrated by Ellis is that self-instruction training is just as effective as instructor training in terms of knowledge of systems features and operations. The cost advantages of self-instruction are obvious. The difficulty in training only by self-instruction is that the customers often have an attitude that self-instruction is not as good as live training. Studies have shown no differences in learning, but a significant effect on users' evaluation of the training itself. Self-instruction training, therefore, must be introduced cautiously for products and services where customers might expect personal training.

While these principles of instruction were developed in studies of business telephones, we feel that they would generalise to a wide range of applications for new technology.

Delivery system

When everyone had a black rotary dial telephone on the desk there were no problems in delivering the right telephone service to the right person. With modern telephone systems, however, there are many options and great complexity. A user of the 'Dimension'® PBX Electronic Custom Telephone Service, for example, can have dozens of features assigned, some conveniently accessible on feature buttons, others available by dial codes. There are an almost limitless number of different feature arrangements possible for each telephone. When a business customer may have hundreds of such telephones, it becomes clear that feature configuration represents a major human factors challenge. The problem is to understand the needs of individual users and to ensure that the right features end up on each telephone. One solution is to make blanket decisions about classes of employees (e.g. secretary, boss, clerk, etc.) and to give each person in a given class the same set of features. While this approach may have some merit, there are two difficulties. First, it is a non-trivial effort to classify people and to develop good feature groupings for each class. Secondly, there will always be many exceptions and their implementation may cause as much trouble as doing the whole job right in the first place.

Duncanson (1980) has demonstrated the feasibility of another approach based on a questionnaire filled out by individual employees or their immediate supervisors. This approach is promising in determining the needs of individual users, but there are still problems to be worked out. The challenge is to make the questionnaire both relevant to the system and comprehensible to the user (who has no knowledge of the new system) without making it as thick as an instruction manual. There are also problems in tailoring the questionnaire to the particular company buying the new system. If not so tailored, the questionnaire may contain many irrelevant and perhaps misleading items.

Little systematic human factors work has been done on delivery systems but there has been enough effort both to identify the need for work and to indicate the large potential of a dedicated program. Indeed, we expect that human factors specialists will be part of the delivery system design team for new systems under development.

Field evaluation

Human factors work on any system is not complete until interviews (and perhaps observations) are made with the eventual users of the system. These studies check the validity of prior decisions, disclose any problems not foreseen in the laboratory, give the best data on feature utility, and disclose user needs for yet other services.

An example of a human factors field evaluation is a study by Dooling in 1977, evaluating customer reaction to the 'Horizon'® Communications System. The 'Horizon' system is an electronic PBX with electronic key telephones for businesses with fewer than 80 telephones. When it was introduced, the first 15 businesses were visited and interviewed about their satisfaction with the system, their feature use, feature knowledge, what they liked and what they didn't like. An attempt was made to interview every user both one week and six weeks after system cutover. At one week, users can still provide fresh information about their adjustment to the new system; by six weeks, most have reached a steady state. Information on user reaction at both stages is relevant to evaluating a system. In conducting such an interview study it is very important to collect systematic data from the actual end users and not rely on the views of the person who purchased the system. Individual users have diverse needs, and products must be designed to meet them as closely as possible. Problems for individual users will eventually become problems for their management.

The survey of over 200 'Horizon' CS users provided a great deal of practical information that was used to fine tune the system. First of all, most users were very satisfied. This finding was critical in the decision to move the system into general introduction after the field trial. Feature use was not as high as we had expected it to be. Originally, we thought that the fact that people do not use all of the features was a training problem. We now view this finding much more broadly. Different users have different needs and no one person needs all of the system features. The issue of feature usage is better directed at the delivery system to ensure that each individual has access to the features needed. Our desk-to-desk interviews asked each individual to tell us two specific things that they liked and two specific things that they did not like. The questions were phrased to force out as many responses as we could get. While this might bias the number of complaints upwards, it did give us a great deal of data. Decisions can then be made on the patterns of likes and dislikes, rather than on their absolute numbers. If one person spontaneously complains about something, we really cannot judge what it means, especially if most people volunteer nothing negative. With the methodology used in this study, however, we can safely ignore most idiosyncratic problems.

As a result of the field evaluation data collected, decisions on the system design could be made intelligently and with some confidence that the trial customer reaction was reasonably representative. As a result, a number of things were changed to improve the 'Horizon' CS service before general introduction. For example, when the system was introduced, calls held at any telephone produced a light 'winking' on and off at the attendant's console. Attendants found this distracting and the 'winking' was eliminated in a new software release.

Another problem concerned the Call Coverage features introduced with the 'Horizon' CS. Most users were very happy with these features and considered them the most valuable in the system. We were surprised, therefore, when several different customers complained vigorously about Call Coverage. Upon investigation it turned out that the features had not been assigned properly. For example, a person's unanswered call might go to the wrong secretary for coverage. To correct this problem, we worked with AT&T Marketing to create an instruction manual for field marketing people to help them understand the appropriate customer applications for coverage. A number of other customer suggestions for improvements were incorporated into the 'Horizon' system and still others were incorporated into planning for new systems for the future. Field evaluations of this sort are necessary steps in good human factors design of products and services. No matter how much experience human factors people have and no matter how many laboratory studies are done, it is necessary to evaluate user reaction to systems under actual field conditions.

Integrating human factors into system design

In addition to the substantive human factors principles which come out of the work illustrated above there are general organisational issues which we think apply in most systems engineering and development activities. (For a broader treatment of such issues, see Dooling and Klemmer, 1982.)

1. It is never too late or too early to make a human factors contribution. Of course, it is best to be involved from the first determination of user needs to the final

evaluation of customer acceptance in the field. But it is possible to begin at any of the phases and have significant impact.

2. The most effective human factors work deals with decisions about to be made. It is difficult to change decisions that have already been made and it is equally difficult to predict decisions very far in advance. Some people should be looking ahead but seldom, if ever, is it possible to anticipate the precise questions needing data for specific engineering decisions.

3. Discovering the human factors issues in any system and influencing decisions require close contact with the systems engineering and development people. Building on knowledge gained from prior similar systems is best done by a continuing association of the human factors specialists with the project team, working in the particular application area. Both of these principles strongly suggest the integration of human factors into the project team on a continuing basis, rather than in a consultant role.

4. Some applied questions can be answered from general human factors principles. More can be answered by data collected on previous systems that are similar. But many important questions require the collection of new data.

5. The collection and analysis of new data often require a laboratory facility capable of quick simulation of proposed features and services. It also requires people trained in quantitative methods, experimental design, and data analysis.

6. Human factors work is complex and requires the most capable people. It requires combined skills from psychology, statistics, engineering and computer science. It is not enough to have expertise in experimental psychology or human factors. The human factors specialist has to be able to talk with the hardware and software people on their own terms and in their own language. A clear understanding of the technical and economic constraints is essential. Such constraints may be cited as reasons why a good human factors design is not possible, but if the human factors specialist is able to delve into the matter and understand the engineering and marketing limitations, an acceptable design can be agreed upon. This approach is greatly expedited by having the engineers and human factors specialists on the same team.

Conclusion

We believe that the examples cited in this paper illustrate the potential contribution of human factors work to all phases of product development from the initial concept of service functions, through hardware and software design, instructions, delivery system, and final field evaluation. These contributions can best be made by integrating human factors people into the working teams at each phase. Organisationally, this implies that human factors people should be part of engineering departments or laboratories, not a large separate entity within an organisation. When human factors work is fully integrated into system design, we believe that maximum effectiveness will be achieved.

References

DOOLING, D.J. (1980). Station user control procedures for business customers: A review of Bell Laboratories findings. In "Proceedings of the ninth international symposium on human factors in telecommunication", Holmdel, New Jersey: Bell Laboratories.

DOOLING, D.J., and KLEMMER, E.T. (1982). New technology for business telephone users: Some findings from human factors studies. In R. A. Kasschau, R. Lachman and K. R. Laughery (Eds). "Information technology and psychology: Prospects for the future", Houston Symposium, Vol. III. New York: Praeger Publishers.

DUNCANSON, J.P. (1980). Letting users specify their own telephone capabilities in complex systems. In "Proceedings of the ninth international symposium on human factors in telecommunication", Holmdel, New Jersey: Bell Laboratories.

ELLIS, S.H. (1977). An investigation of telephone user training methods for a multi-service electronic PBX. In "Proceedings of the eighth international symposium on human factors in telecommunications", Harlow, Essex, England: Standard Telecommunication Laboratories.

ELLIS, S.H., and COSKREN, R.A. (1979). *Bell Laboratories Record*, **57**, 60–65. New approach to customer training.

HANSON, B.L. (1983). *Bell System Technical Journal*, A brief history of applied behavioural science at Bell Laboratories, in press.

Index